SOB
SOB
£3.30

The BASH STREET KIDS BOOK 1991

Printed and Published in Great Britain by D. C. THOMSON & CO., LTD.,
185 Fleet Street, London, EC4A 2HS.

ISBN 0 85116 484 6

LOOK OUT
BANG

ALL CHANGE
GLOOM!
WE HATE GOING TO SCHOOL.
WHAT ABOUT ME? I'M SO NERVOUS ABOUT TEACHING THE KIDS . . .
MOAN! I'M GIVEN ALL THE WORK AROUND HERE!
HERE!
TASKS
HEAD 1
MEMO TO WINSTON THE CAT
DO THESE JOBS PRONTO
SIGNED Janitor
AND I DO ALL THE WORK AROUND HERE!
I'M FED UP HAVING MY COOKING CRITICISED!
OLIVE
YEUGH!
FULL
NOT SUCH A GOOD IDEA AFTER ALL!
I must not be so stupid
Then—
CLASS II B
JANITOR
AH! HERE'S MY TEA.
WHERE IS IT?
SLURP! MUST HAVE EVAPORATED!
Meanwhile—
WINSTON'S JOB'S FINE!
SQUEAK!
YEEOW! I'VE CHANGED MY MIND!
JAB
I DON'T MIND DOING OLIVE'S COOKING . . .

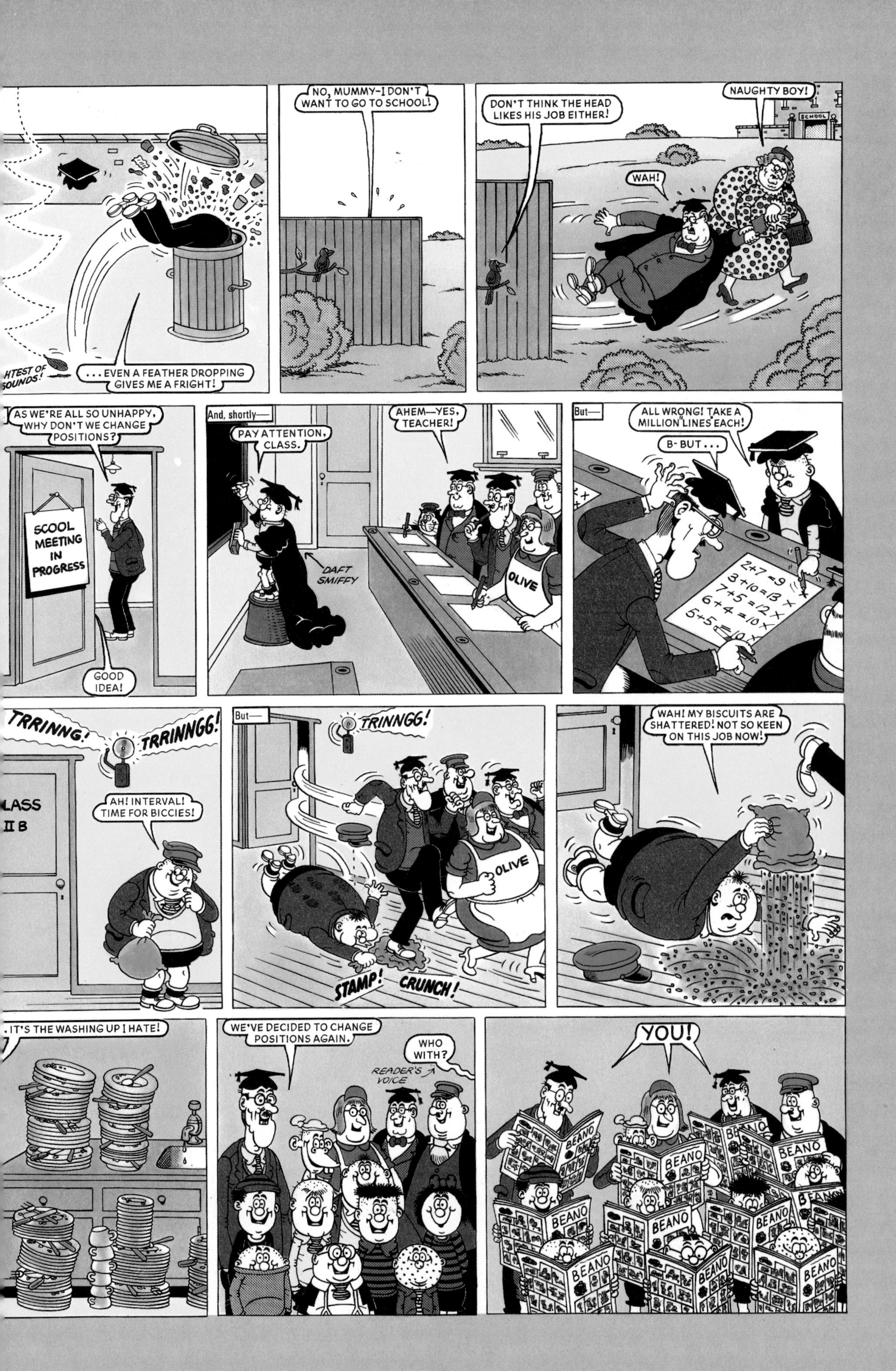

HTEST OF SOUNDS!
. . . EVEN A FEATHER DROPPING GIVES ME A FRIGHT!
NO, MUMMY—I DON'T WANT TO GO TO SCHOOL!
DON'T THINK THE HEAD LIKES HIS JOB EITHER!
NAUGHTY BOY!
SCHOOL
WAH!
AS WE'RE ALL SO UNHAPPY, WHY DON'T WE CHANGE POSITIONS?
SCOOL MEETING IN PROGRESS
GOOD IDEA!
And, shortly—
PAY ATTENTION, CLASS.
AHEM—YES, TEACHER!
DAFT SMIFFY
OLIVE
But—
ALL WRONG! TAKE A MILLION LINES EACH!
B- BUT . . .
2+7 = 9
3+10 = 13 X
7+5 = 12 X
6+4 = 10 X
5+5 = 10 X
TRRINNG!
TRRINNGG!
LASS
II B
AH! INTERVAL! TIME FOR BICCIES!
But—
TRINNGG!
OLIVE
STAMP!
CRUNCH!
WAH! MY BISCUITS ARE SHATTERED! NOT SO KEEN ON THIS JOB NOW!
. IT'S THE WASHING UP I HATE!
WE'VE DECIDED TO CHANGE POSITIONS AGAIN.
WHO WITH?
READER'S VOICE
YOU!
BEANO

Disguise Surprise
ROVERS v. UNITED
KICK-OFF 3·00 P.M.
THAT'LL BE A GREAT MATCH.
PITY WE COULDN'T GET THE AFTERNOON OFF TO SEE IT.
SCRUFFY LOT! WHY CAN'T YOU BE MORE LIKE YOUR TEACHER?
SCRUFFY? I HA A BATH AT CHRISTMAS!
BASH STREET SCHOOL
Later—
HERE COMES TEACHER! KEEP THOSE COSTUMES OUT OF SIGHT!
GOOD DAY, CHILDREN. VERY HOT TODAY!
CLASS II B
HI, TEACHER!
TODAY I WILL TEACH YOU ABOUT TURKEY.
CHALK
MAPS OF THE WORLD
YUMMY! FOOD'S MY FAVOURITE SUBJECT!
PHEW! THE HEAT MUST BE AFFECTING ME!
TUG
MUSTN'T LET THE CLASS SEE I'M UPSET.
NOW WE WILL—ERK!
WAH!
I'M NOT WELL! TAKE THE AFTERNOON OFF!
YIPPEE! JUST AS WE PLANNED!

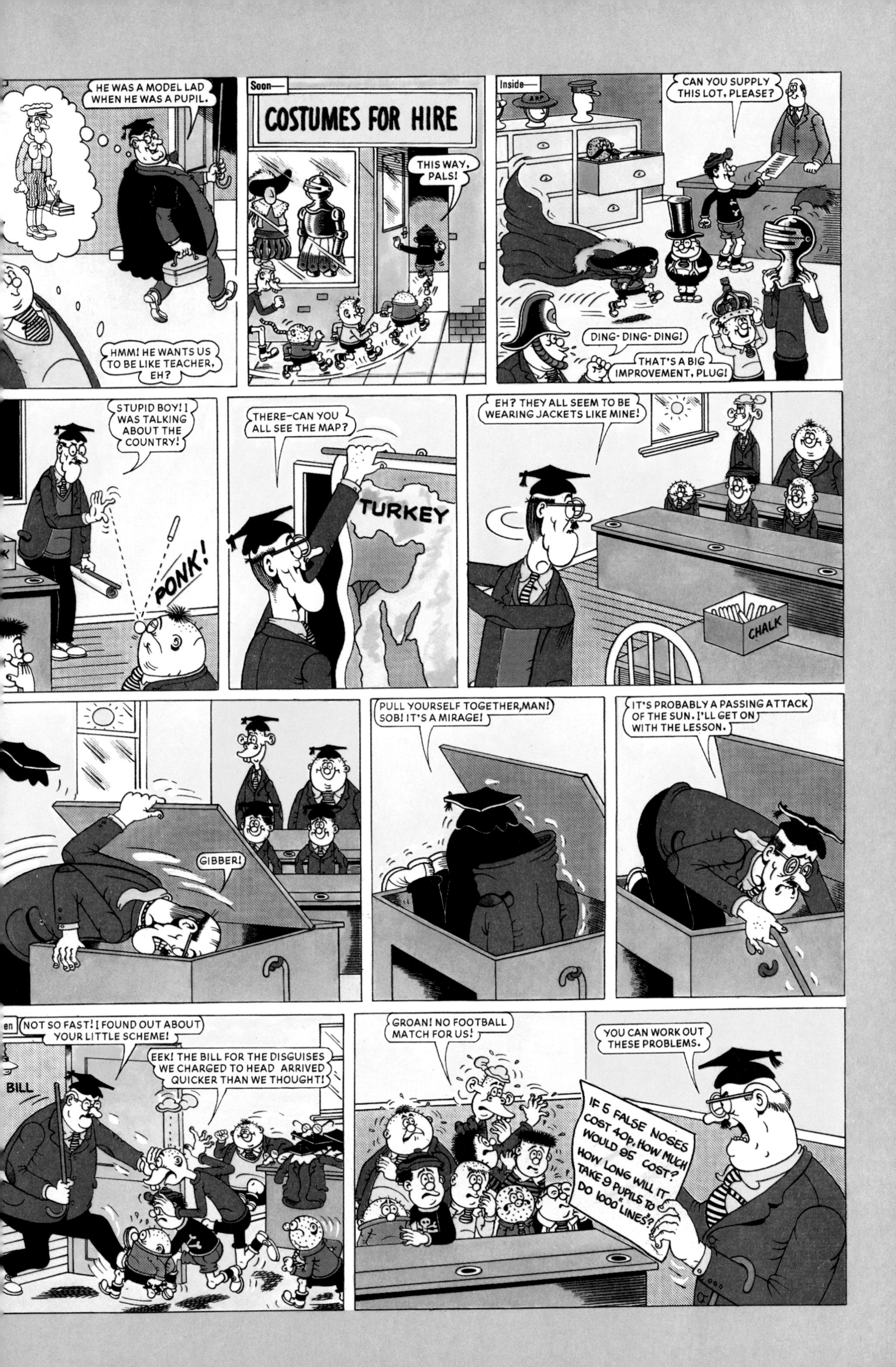

HE WAS A MODEL LAD WHEN HE WAS A PUPIL.
HMM! HE WANTS US TO BE LIKE TEACHER, EH?
Soon—
COSTUMES FOR HIRE
THIS WAY, PALS!
Inside—
CAN YOU SUPPLY THIS LOT, PLEASE?
DING-DING-DING!
THAT'S A BIG IMPROVEMENT, PLUG!
STUPID BOY! I WAS TALKING ABOUT THE COUNTRY!
PONK!
THERE—CAN YOU ALL SEE THE MAP?
TURKEY
EH? THEY ALL SEEM TO BE WEARING JACKETS LIKE MINE!
CHALK
GIBBER!
PULL YOURSELF TOGETHER, MAN! SOB! IT'S A MIRAGE!
IT'S PROBABLY A PASSING ATTACK OF THE SUN. I'LL GET ON WITH THE LESSON.
NOT SO FAST! I FOUND OUT ABOUT YOUR LITTLE SCHEME!
BILL
EEK! THE BILL FOR THE DISGUISES WE CHARGED TO HEAD ARRIVED QUICKER THAN WE THOUGHT!
GROAN! NO FOOTBALL MATCH FOR US!
YOU CAN WORK OUT THESE PROBLEMS.
IF 5 FALSE NOSES COST 40p, HOW MUCH WOULD 95 COST? HOW LONG WILL IT TAKE 9 PUPILS TO DO 1000 "LINES"?

CAT of all TRADES
In the Head's office—
BEANO
TRINNG!
TRINNG!
..THIS IS TEACHER HERE—SNIFFLE!..
JANITOR HERE—COUGH!..
So—
SCHOOL
AACHOO! I'M OFF HOME!
COUGH! ME, TOO!
OLIVE
YOU'LL HAVE TO TAKE OVER, WINSTON!
YES, SIR!
YOU'LL NEED THESE HATS FOR YOUR NEW JOBS.
13 KIPPERS + 17 KIPPERS = AN AWFUL SMELL.
27 MICE + 11 MICE = LOTS OF HOLES IN THE WALL.
22 SAUCERS OF MILK − 18 SAUCERS OF MILK =
A FULL TUM FOR FATTY.
NAUGHTY BOY! MUST PUNISH HIM!
So—
GULP!
But—
LUNCH
TIME
ERK! LOOK AT THE TIME!
WE'RE STARVING!
GASP! GOT TO SERVE LUNCH NOW!
WHEW! PUFF!
WHAT ABOUT SECONDS?
CLASS IIB
WHEEZE! GIBBER! THIS IS TOO MUCH WORK FOR ONE CAT!

. . . I'M DOWN WITH "FLU"!
SO AM I!
FLU BUG
AH! ANOTHER VICTIM!
HEH-HEH! WE CAME THROUGH THE 'PHONE LINES!
JAB!
OH, DEAR—SNEEZE!—NOW I'VE CAUGHT A GERM!
ACHOOO!
FIRST, SOME TEACHING . . .
13 KIPPERS + 17 KIPPERS =
27 MICE + 11 MICE =
22 SAUCERS OF MILK — 18 SAUCERS OF MILK =
SNATCH
I KNOW THE ANSWERS!
'VE THE JANITOR'S JOB TO DO NOW!
DRING!
TRING!
CLANG!
BING!
LUNCH BELL
AFTERNOON BELL
CLICK!
PANT! GASP!
DINING HALL
TODAY'S CHOICE
TAKE IT OR LEAVE IT
ZOOM!
NOW TO MAKE THE LUNCHES! WHEEZE!
JUST A MINUTE—I'M HEAD AS WELL! THAT MEANS . . .
HEAD'S HAT
BOX OF HATS
BOX OF HATS
. . . I CAN GIVE EVERYONE A HALF-DAY!
PITY WINSTON WASN'T IN CHARGE ALL THE TIME!

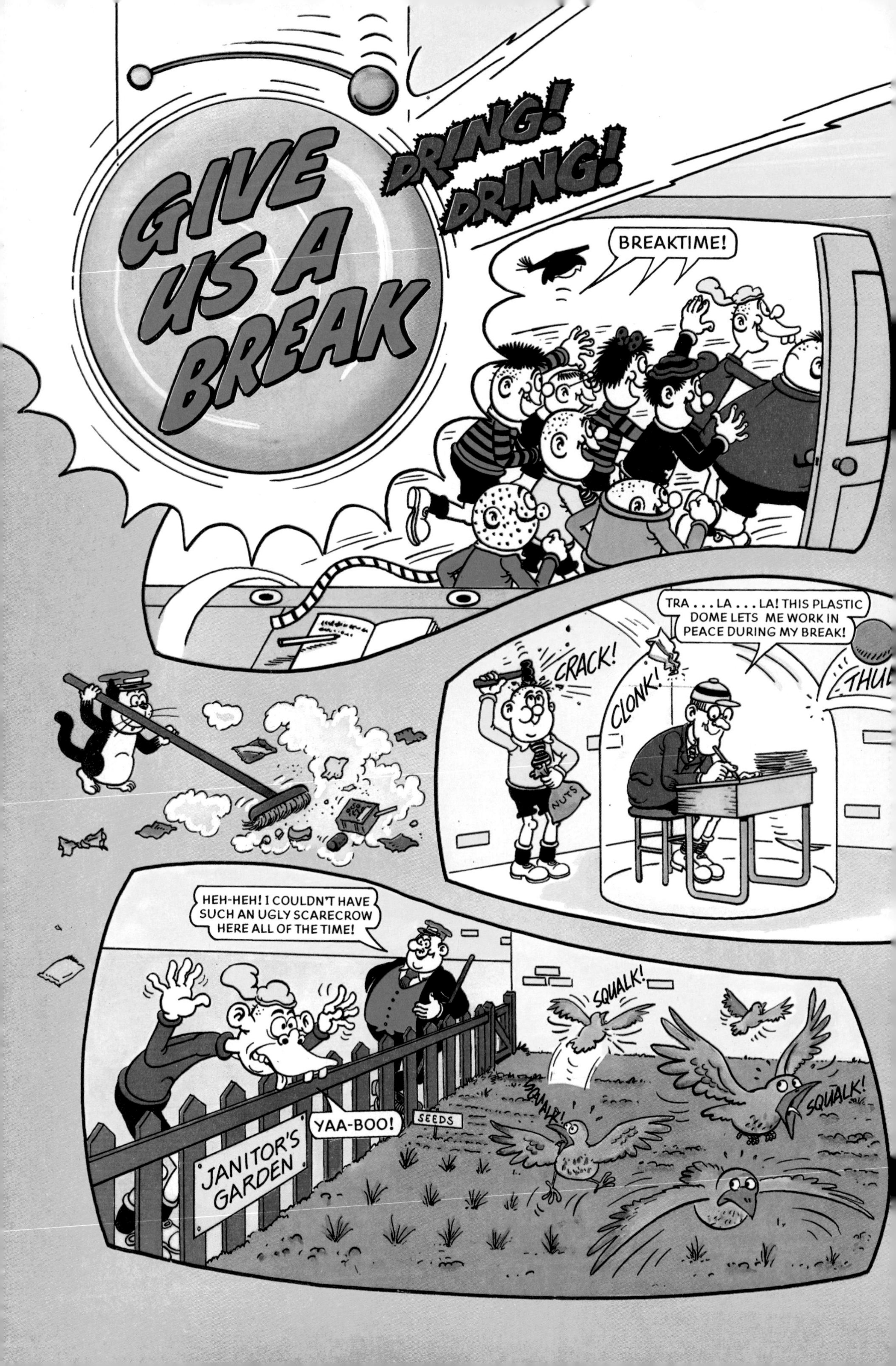

GIVE US A BREAK
DRING! DRING!
BREAKTIME!
TRA . . . LA . . . LA! THIS PLASTIC DOME LETS ME WORK IN PEACE DURING MY BREAK!
CRACK!
CLONK!
NUTS
HEH-HEH! I COULDN'T HAVE SUCH AN UGLY SCARECROW HERE ALL OF THE TIME!
SQUALK!
SQUALK!
YAA-BOO!
SEEDS
JANITOR'S GARDEN

SAM'S CHIP SHOP
HOT DONUTS
CHOMP! MUNCH! JUST WHAT I ORDERED FOR MY BREAKTIME SNACK! GOBBLE!
HAW-HAW! BEST WAY TO HAVE A BREAK — WITH A BEANO! CHORTLE!
During the break in the 'Staff Room' —
YOU WILL GO BACK TO CLASS AFTER THE BREAK! YOU ARE NOT SCARED OF THOSE BRATS!
GIBBER!

BUS FUSS
This is Gilbert Splunge—it's his birthday today.
GROAN! GASP!
HAPPY TWENTY-FIRST BIRTHDAY, SON!
WHEEZE! PUFF!
CORN FLAKES
21st
IT'S QUICKER BY TRAIN
LUGGAGE ONLY
I'LL HIDE IN HERE!
But—
IT'S QUICKER BY TRAIN
LUGGAGE ONLY
OO! GROAN!
THROB
EEK!
WE'VE GIVEN HIM A LIFT OK—RIGHT OFF THE GROUND!
Soon—
COME AND SEE MY PET MOUSE, WILFRED.
HOI! OUCH!
WAH! THANK GOODNESS THEY'VE GONE!
SCHOOL
WOW! I LIKE YOUR EARRINGS, TEACHER!
THEY'RE NOT EARRINGS—THEY'RE ICICLES—THE HEATING'S BROKEN DOWN!
SNAP!
SNAP!

ASP! WHY DO YOU LOOK SO OLD?
READER'S VOICE
YOU'D LOOK OLD, TOO . . .
. . . IF YOU WERE THE CONDUCTOR ON THE BASH STREET SCHOOL BUS!
CONDUCTOR
Later—
HERE THEY COME! MUST HIDE!
WAHEY!
RIGHT—LET ME SEE YOUR BUS PASSES.
HOW ARE THESE FOR PASSES?
BONK!
PASS
HEH-HEH!
Soon—
AH, THE HEADMASTER! BETTER GIVE HIM A LIFT.
AY ATTENTION TO THAT NOTICE IN FUTURE!
PLEASE MIND YOUR HEAD WHEN LEAVING SEAT
SORRY, HEAD!
At school—
KINDLY LEAVE IN AN ORDERLY MANNER.
ZOOM!
YAHOO!
SCHOOL BUS
WHEEZE! GASP!
CAN'T TEACH IN THESE CONDITIONS. AH! JUST A MINUTE . . .
WAH! BOO-HOO! I THOUGHT I'D GOT RID OF THEM FOR THE DAY! WAIL!
THIS IS REALLY A SCHOOL BUS NOW!
3 × 3 × 4 =

STARSTRUCK
HOROSCOPES BY GYPSY ROSE OLIVE
Don't be surprised if something you do irritates your friends. Your lucky colour is red and lucky number 11B.
CAPRICORN SMIFFY
11B BASH St.
SURF KING
OIL
USED TICKETS
SURF TUM!
SOLARIUM
You'll have a smashing time on a day out. Your unlucky number is seven (years bad luck).
SMASH!
SSSSMASH!
CRASHH!
AQUARIUS~PLUG

STARS for a DAY
HERE'S THE CREW TO FILM US FOR 'A DAY IN THE LIFE OF BASH STREET SCHOOL'. JUST ACT NORMAL!
TV UNIT
TV FILM CREW
OH, BOY! BASH STREET ON THE TELLY!
WOW! US — TV STARS!
So — make up —
MAKE UP VAN
WOO! WOO! WAA!
— lights —
CHORTLE!
— sound —
TESTING! TESTING! 1 . . . 2 . . . 4 . . . 3 . . .
EEK!
SCREECH!
BLARE!
—filming.
WELL, IT'S THE QUIETEST THEY'VE BEEN ALL DAY! I MUST GET A CAMERA IN HERE MORE OFTEN! HA-HA!
STIFF WITH STAGE FRIGHT!
WHIRR!
WE'RE BEING FILMED!
OH, NO! I'M SCARED!

A LOAD OF RUBBISH
At interval—
VERY DULL OUTSIDE TODAY.
Outside—
SCHOOL
EH? IT'S SUNNY! BUT HOW?
THANKS! THE WIND BLEW THIS RUBBISH OVER ME.
AN AWFUL LOT OF RUBBISH ABOUT.
Inside—
AN ESCAPED SNAKE!
HEAD'S STUDY
HISSSSS
HISSS
DON'T WORRY, HEAD I'LL GET THE NASTY SNAKE FOR YOU
UP YOU GET AND GET ON WITH SOME WORK, IDLE MAN!
OO-ER! YES, YOUR HEADSHIP—RIGHT AWAY!
PULL
BUMP!
BEANO
So—
PUFF! PANT!
And soon—
GASP! WHAT A HEAT IN HERE!
WAFT!
HEAT WAVES
WARP
PANT!
I'LL CLEAR UP THE PLAYGROUND NEXT.
CHUG! CHUG!
R-U-M-B-L-E!
CHUG! CHUG!
AH! THERE'S MORE RUBBISH!
Then—
HEY! WHERE'S MY BIKE?

THIS WINDOW'S FILTHY! NO WONDER IT SEEMED DULL!
WHERE'S SPOTTY?
HELP! HELP!
EH?
HISSSSS!
IT'S NOT A SNAKE—IT'S THAT RADIATOR! THE JANITOR'S BEEN PROMISING TO FIX IT FOR AGES.
HMM! THE JANITOR'S BEEN FALLING BEHIND WITH A LOT OF HIS DUTIES.
I'LL HAVE A WORD WITH HIM.
BOILER ROOM
THERE HE IS, THE LAZY FELLOW!
BEANO
MY ICED-LOLLY'S MELTED!
WILT
Outside—
MUST CLEAN THE WINDOW NOW.
WE NEED AIR IN HERE! CROAK!
THROW
SPLOOSH!
WAH!
ER—IS THIS IT?
SHRIEK!
HUH! THINGS WERE FAR BETTER WHEN THE JANITOR WAS BEING LAZY!
So—
HAVE MY NICE, COMFY CHAIR, OLD CHAP!
PUT YOUR FEET UP AND READ THE "BEANO BOOK" I GOT FOR CHRISTMAS!
BEANO
CREAM CAKES
SWEETS

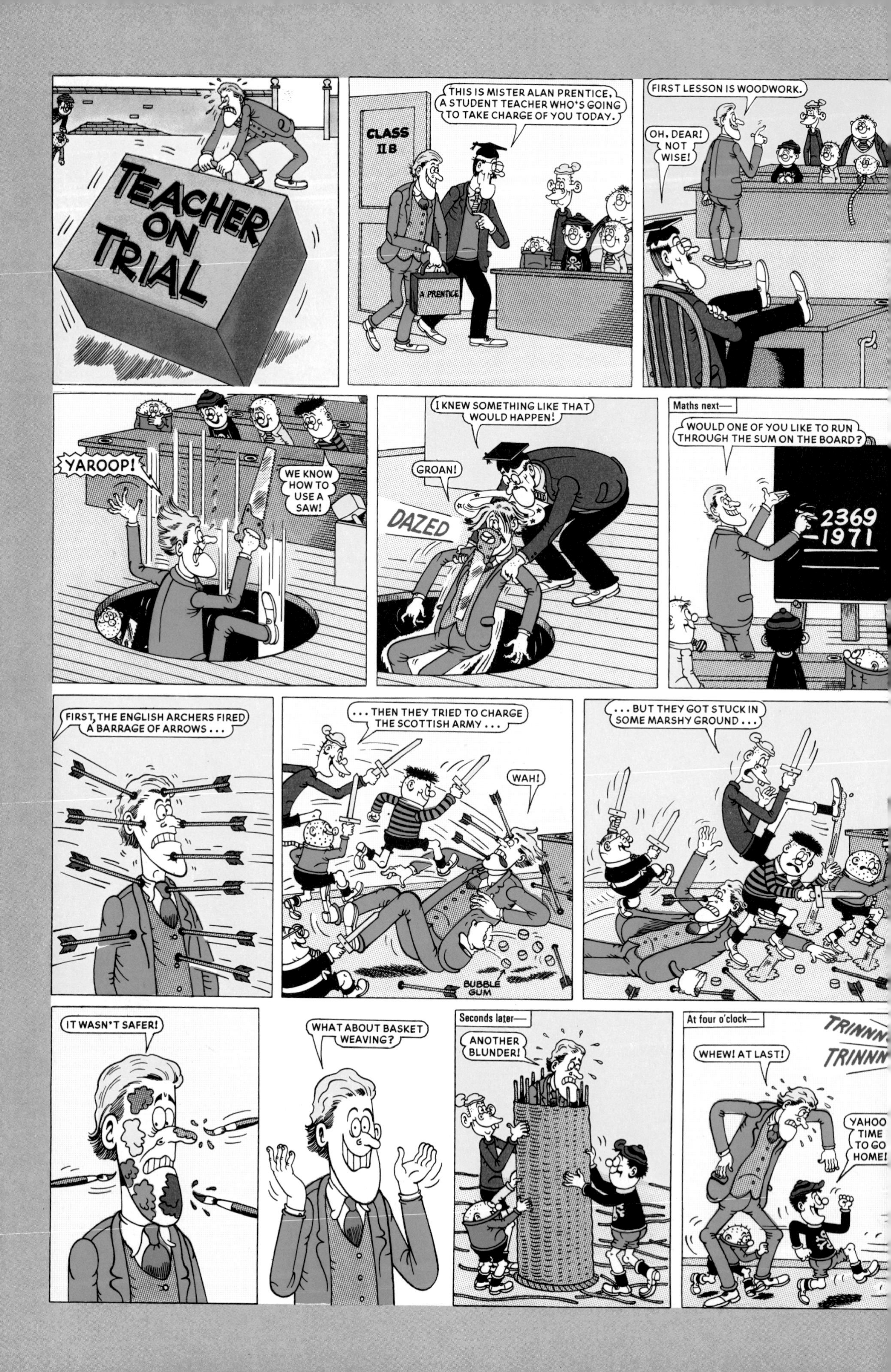
TEACHER ON TRIAL
THIS IS MISTER ALAN PRENTICE, A STUDENT TEACHER WHO'S GOING TO TAKE CHARGE OF YOU TODAY.
CLASS IIB
A PRENTICE
FIRST LESSON IS WOODWORK.
OH, DEAR! NOT WISE!
YAROOP!
WE KNOW HOW TO USE A SAW!
I KNEW SOMETHING LIKE THAT WOULD HAPPEN!
GROAN!
DAZED
Maths next—
WOULD ONE OF YOU LIKE TO RUN THROUGH THE SUM ON THE BOARD?
2369
-1971
FIRST, THE ENGLISH ARCHERS FIRED A BARRAGE OF ARROWS ...
... THEN THEY TRIED TO CHARGE THE SCOTTISH ARMY ...
WAH!
BUBBLE GUM
... BUT THEY GOT STUCK IN SOME MARSHY GROUND ...
IT WASN'T SAFER!
WHAT ABOUT BASKET WEAVING?
Seconds later—
ANOTHER BLUNDER!
At four o'clock—
TRINNN
TRINNN
WHEW! AT LAST!
YAHOO TIME TO GO HOME!

HEH-HEH!
SQUEAK!
UNDER I GO!
NOW I'LL SHOW YOU HOW TO USE A SAW PROPERLY.
TOOLS
BZZZZ!
GOOD BOY!
ME! ME! ME!
THICK-HEADED SMIFFY
ERK!
2369 -1971
THERE! I'VE RUN THROUGH IT FOR YOU!
ZOOM!
ZOOM!
Next—
HISTORY NOW—WHAT DO YOU KNOW ABOUT THE BATTLE OF BANNOCKBURN?
SO ROBERT THE BRUCE LED HIS MEN DOWN FROM THE HILLS . . .
. . . AND THE ENGLISH ADMITTED DEFEAT— YES, JUST LIKE THAT!
WAVE
PERHAPS ART MIGHT BE SAFER.
OO-ER!
CLASS II B
CHEER!
YOU'VE EARNED YOUR MORTAR-BOARD— ANYONE WHO CAN LAST A DAY WITH THE BASH STREET KIDS DESERVES TO BE A TEACHER!
ANYONE WHO'S LASTED A DAY WITH THE BASH STREET KIDS DOESN'T WANT TO BE A TEACHER!
CLASS II B

PAST MASTER
THIS SCHOOL'S NEEDING NEW EQUIPMENT.
WHAT MAKES YOU SAY THAT?
LOOK AT THE MARKINGS ON MY DESK!
HMM!
JULIUS CAESAR SAT HERE
CROMP!
CHOMP!
. . . THAT THE MOTHS IN THEM HAVE GROWN LONG WHITE BEARDS!
WE'VE USED THE SAME PENCILS FOR FIVE YEARS—CAN WE GET NEW ONES?
DRAW
PENCILS
WE MUST GET NEW EQUIPMENT!
I'LL SEE WHAT'S IN THE SCHOOL KITTY.
HANDSOME CHAP, THAT!
WINSTON BANK
WOOPEE! IT'S FULL OF CASH!
SHAKE
But—
BAH! TEN SHILLING NOTES, THREEPENNY PIECES AND FARTHINGS! EVEN THE MONEY'S OUT OF DATE!
Soon—
HEH-HEH! WORKED A TREAT—ALL THE TICKETS SOLD!
That night—
DISCO TONIGHT
TEACHER SAID HE'D ORGANISE THE MUSIC AND LIGHT SHOW.
OH, GOODY!
But—
OH, NO!
DISCO THIS WAY

THEN THERE ARE OUR ANCIENT ATLASES . .
ATLAS
JUST LOOK AT THIS!
GOSH! YOU'RE RIGHT!
AMERICA
NOT DISCOVERED YET
AND OUR SCHOOL FOOTBALL STRIPS ARE SO OLD . . .
ONE LEFT, I'M AFRAID— BUT NEVER MIND . . .
. . . YOU CAN HAVE THESE!
BAH! NOW WE'VE GONE BACK TO THE STONE AGE!
WRONG ANSWERS
THUD
THICK HEADED SMIFFY BROKE HIS HAMMER
BONK!
Smiffy was Here
ET'S HOLD A DISCO TO
AISE MONEY FOR NEW EQUIPMENT!
GOOD THINKING!
Later—
HOW ARE WE GOING TO GET THE DISCO TICKETS SOLD?
NO TROUBLE—FORM A QUEUE.
BASH ST. SCHOOL
BASH ST. SCHOOL
So—
LOOK—A QUEUE! MUST BE FOR SOMETHING GOOD!
BASH ST.
LET'S JOIN IT!
COME INTO THE GARDEN, MAUDE...
LOVELY!
SNARL!
GRR! SELL US TICKETS FOR THIS ROTTEN DISCO, WOULD YOU? OOF!
THUMP!
BASH!
BIFF!
I'LL NEVER UNDERSTAND THESE MODERN DANCES!

HAIR AFFAIR
TUM-TIDDLE-TUM!
TIME WE WERE MAKING NESTS.
BETTER GET SOME STUFF TO BUILD THEM.
ERK!
WHAT ABOUT A NEW STYLE OF MOUSTACHE?
AND FRECKLES?
A BEARD, MAYBE?
AARGH! I LOOK HORRIBLE!
WE'VE SAID THAT FOR YEARS!
MIRROR
HAVE TO THINK OF ANOTHER WAY TO REPLACE MY MOUSTACHE.
WHAT ABOUT COTTON WOOL?
BUT IT DOESN'T MATCH THE COLOUR OF MY HAIR!
COTTON WOOL
FLOUR
IT MATCHES NOW, OK!
FLUMP!
GRR! CAN'T HAVE THIS!
TRINNNG!
YAHOO!
LUNCH-TIME—TO THE DINNER HALL.
In the dinner hall—
A NICE SALAD, TEACHER—PREPARED BY MY OWN FAIR HAND.
OLIVE
LOVELY!
But—
EH?

PYONG!
R-I-P!
EEARGH!
HAW-HAW! YOU LOOK ODD WITHOUT YOUR MOUSTACHE, TEACHER!
WAH! WHAT CAN I DO TILL IT GROWS IN AGAIN?
In class—
NOT TO WORRY—WE'LL HELP YOU.
I'LL GET YOU A NICE MOUSTACHE, TEACHER.
PEA-BRAINED SMIFFY
Soon—
RUBBISH DUMP
AH! THERE IT IS!
Shortly—
I'VE GOT IT!
GOODY!
GROAN!
A "HANDLEBAR" MOUSTACHE! SMART, EH?
TING-A-LING!
THIS HAIR-RESTORER SHOULD DO THE TRICK.
HAIR RESTORER
But—
TRIP
OOPS!
HOW TO GROW A MOUSTACHE
HAIR RESTORER
Then—
PITY THE BOTTLE'S FINISHED—IT SEEMS TO WORK!
HOW TO GROW A MOUSTACHE
H, DEAR! TEACHER WILL BE FURIOUS!
I, THERE!
WELL DONE, GOOD WOMAN!
GOSH!
CUDDLE
RATHER DASHING, DON'T YOU THINK?

Teacher rules O.K
Teacher's on his way to school—
HOW WONDERFUL IT WOULD BE TO HAVE THE HEADMASTER'S JOB.
A DOG BEGGING
BICCY BARREL
TEA
DO NOT DISTURB
ALL HE DOES IS LAZE AROUND ALL DAY . . .
So—
I WON'T BE TEACHING YOU TODAY—I'M THE HEADMASTER!
In the Head's study—
AH! THIS IS THE LIFE!
In the classroom—
HEH- HEH! LET'S PLAY A TRICK ON TEACHER!
WHAT'S YOUR PLAN?
MY BOY . . . SHODDY WORK . . . TERRIBLE MANNERS . . . RUDE AND UNCOUTH . . . MOAN ! . . GRUMBLE!
ER—YES—ALL TEACHER'S FAULT—I'LL HAVE HIM FLOGGED.
PHEW! I MUST REMEMBER TO THROW THIS BOOK AWAY BEFORE THE HEAD RETURNS!
GREAT SO FAR, KIDS! NOW FOR YOUR NEW DISGUISE!
INSPECTOR
. . . GHASTLY!
SORRY, TEACHER! NOT MUCH GOOD, IS IT?
SUPPOSE AN INSPECTOR SAW IT?
I'LL HAVE TO DO ALL THE WORK FOR THE INSPECTOR TO SEE!
I'VE GOT SOME MORE PAPER, TEACHER.
INK
HERE'S MORE INK FOR YOU!
At last—
GASP! I'M EXHAUSTED!

...WHILE I HAVE TO PUT UP WITH WHAT'S BEHIND THAT DOOR!
YAHOO!
CLASS II B
TERRIFIC DIN!
NOISY DISTURBANCE!
HMM! I WONDER WHAT THIS NOTE SAYS?
CLASS II B
YIPPEE! MY DREAM'S COME TRUE!
R-I-P!
HAD TO GO TO SOUTH OF FRANCE IN A HURRY. YOU'RE IN CHARGE TODAY.
Headmaster
THIS OLD CAP AND COAT WILL DO THE TRICK!
AND HERE'S A BEARD AND MOUSTACHE FOR YOU!
Soon—
OO-ER! THAT COULD BE A PARENT—I'D BETTER LOOK AT THE BOOK OF RULES IN CASE.
KNOCK! KNOCK!
HOW TO BE A HEAD
I'VE GOT A COMPLAINT, HEADMASTER!
HEAD'S STUDY
IT SAYS HERE..."IF IT GOES RIGHT, IT WAS YOU—IF NOT, BLAME IT ON TEACHER!"
resently—
I HEAR YOU FLOG YOUR TEACHERS, HEADMASTER—THAT'S AGAINST THE RULES!
OH, NO—A CHOOL INSPECTOR!
INSPECTOR
I'LL BE BACK TO LOOK AT THE KIDS' WORK. IF IT'S GOOD, I'LL LET YOU OFF. IF NOT...
GULP!
OH, DEAR! I KNOW ONLY TOO WELL WHAT THE KIDS' WORK'S LIKE...
WHAT'S THAT YOU'RE FANNING HIM WITH, SMIFFY?
SO! A SCHOOL INSPECTOR, EH? I'VE BEEN TRICKED!
OOPS! SILLY ME!
AND WHERE DO YOU THINK YOU'RE GOING?
THE SOUTH OF FRANCE WITH THE HEAD! THINGS ARE GETTING TOO HOT FOR US HERE!

MONSTER MIRTH
THE NEXT PICTURE'S NOT FOR READERS OF A NERVOUS NATURE!
THE LOCH NESS MONSTER, OR "NESSIE"—PEOPLE COME FROM MILES AROUND TO SEE HER!
HANDSOME BRUTE!
WE'LL STUFF THIS OLD MATTRESS AND MAKE "BASHIE" FAT LIKE ME!
OLD MATTRESS
So—
THERE—HE'S LOOKING MORE LIKE A MONSTER ALREADY!
WHAT SORT OF FACE WILL WE GIVE HIM?
LEAVE IT TO ME—I'LL GIVE HIM A BEAUTIFUL FACE.
I EXPECT "BASHIE'S" A BIT SHORT-SIGHTED LIKE ME—THESE SPECS SHOULD HELP!
I. BLINK OPTICIAN
NOW "BASHIE" CAN SEE WHERE HE'S GOING!
HO-HO! HE MUST TAKE AFTER TEACHER THEN—EYES IN THE BACK OF HIS HEAD!
"BASHIE" SHOULD HAVE LONG HAIR LIKE ME!
NO—SHORT AND SPIKY LIKE MINE
Meanwhile—
IT'S TAKEN ME DAYS TO CLEAN OUT THE POND LIKE YOU ASKED ME.
ASSISTANT PARK KEEPER
I'LL INSPECT YOUR WORK.
HEAD PARK KEEPER
Has "Bashie" frightened them?
EEK!
YIKES!
No!
SNARL! ALL MY HARD WORK WASTED!
BASH STREET POND

EXPECT PEOPLE WOULD FLOCK TO SEE A BASH STREET POND MONSTER, OR " BASHIE "!
I WONDER WHAT HE'D LOOK LIKE?
BASH STREET POND
BOYLK!
I'M SURE HE'D BE VERY FAT AND VERY UGLY!
COME ON—WE CAN MAKE A SUPER MONSTER FROM THIS STUFF LYING AROUND!
OK, PLUG.
THAT FACE WILL FRIGHTEN EVERYONE!
CHEEK!
HOW GHASTLY!
THERE'S ONLY ONE THING NEEDED TO MAKE " BASHIE " A GREAT MONSTER!
WHAT'S THAT?
SPLAT!
SPLAT!
SPLAT!
LOTS OF SPOTS! THAT'S MORE LIKE IT!
I'LL SHOW HIM! THIS ROPE MAKES SUPER LONG STRANDS OF HAIR!
I'LL SHOW HER! THIS CHIMNEY SWEEP'S BRUSH IS FINE AND SPIKY!
I. BLINK OPTICIAN
When " Bashie " is finished—
WE NAME YOU " BASHIE ", AND MAY YOU FRIGHTEN ALL WHO SEE YOU!
I. BLINK OPTICIAN
YOUR TEACHER SHALL HEAR OF THIS!
READER'S VOICE
SEEN A MONSTER, KIDS?
OO!
EEK!
WAH!
EXTRA HOMEWORK
27 ×9
438 +726
7)427
43 +81
97 ×11
635 421 +876
69 ×8
NO, READER—THAT'S WHAT FRIGHTENS US MORE THAN ANY MONSTER!

Thanks for Pranks
TEE-HEE! WAIT TILL TEACHER COMES IN!
FLOUR
HEH-HEH!
But—
TOPPLE
MIXING BOWL
CLASS II B
TEE-TUM!
Later—
TRA-LA-LA!
WE'LL SOAK TEACHER WITH THAT BALLOON FULL OF WATER WE HUNG UP WHEN HE WASN'T LOOKING!
RIGHT ON TARGET!
PRANG!
HEH-HEH! THANKS FOR WATERING MY PLANTS! TOLD YOU I'D GET THE BETTER OF YOU!
SWOOSH!
. . . FIRE!
TWANG!
TWANG!
TWANG!
TWANG!
TWANG!
SPLAT!
SPLOT!
SPLUT!
EXCELLENT—I WANTED YOU TO TRY SOME MODERN ART!
TEE-HEE-HEE! I'VE COME OUT ON TOP THIS WEEK!
Enter the Headmaster—
WHAT HAVE YOU PUPILS BEEN UP TO TODAY?
WE HELPED TEACHER MAKE SCONES.
WE WATERED TEACHER'S PLANTS
WE DID A LOVELY PAINTING.
THEN WE FOUND SPLENDID EXHIB FOR OUR BIOLOG LESSON.

MAKE ME SOME SCONES FOR INTERVAL, WOULD YOU, OLIVE?
CERTAINLY.
SCHOOL COOK
BAH! TEACHER WAS EXPECTING THAT!
YOU'LL NOT GET THE BETTER OF ME— I KNOW ALL YOUR PRANKS!
THAT'S A CHALLENGE WE CAN'T RESIST!
HERE ARE SOME JARS OF PAINT— GET ON AND DO SOME PAINTINGS.
WE'LL BOMBARD TEACHER WITH COLOURED PELLETS!
DIP
DIP
DIP
READY, AIM...
ERE'S AN APPLE FOR YOU, SIR.
HMM!
JUST WHAT I WANTED...
THUMP!
PTCHEE!
...WE'RE STUDYING INSECTS IN BIOLOGY TODAY!
GASP! IS THIS TRUE?
ER—WELL—YES...
SO GLAD TO HEAR OF SUCH DILIGENCE. NO HOMEWORK FOR YOU FOR A WEEK!
PAT!
PAT!
SMUG EXPRESSIONS
SNORT! THEY'VE GOT THE BETTER OF ME AFTER ALL! GROWL!

STARSTRUCK
HOROSCOPES BY GYPSY ROSE OLIVE
PISCES~DANNY
SOOT
A tall dark stranger will cross your path. Your lucky colour is NOT black and your lucky number is NOT 1,000 (lines).
PLUG IS HANDSUM
Now's your chance to get away from it all. You will meet lots of interesting people.
ZOOOMM!
WAAAA!
BUS STOP
DINK!
ARIES~HEADMASTER

Special Delivery
WITH THE BASH STREET PUPS :-
It's nearly time to pounce on the postman, Pups!
HERE GOES! GRRR!
Hey! Where are you going, Postie?
I'm tired of being ambushed by you lot ~ deliver the mail yourselves!
Oh, dear! Looks like Postie wins today.
MAIN STREET
HIGH STREET
LOW STREET
I'll deliver this one.
Where on Earth's he going?
This must be the way.
TO THE EAST
Ed's note:- "END" MISSING!
MILES LATER ~
Can't be far now.
It must be on the other side of this great wall.
Up I go.
But the gate's open!
OVER THE WALL ~
Must be here, somewhere.
YAHOO! I can deliver my parcel now!
STICKS CHOPPED HERE
Arf! Arf! You really are the daftest pup ever, Sniffy!
I am?...
... over the Great Wall, where the chopsticks are ~ isn't that China?
China's what's inside ~ not the address!
FRAGILE
CHINA

CREEPY CRAWLY FOLLY
TODAY, FOR BIOLOGY, WE SHALL LOOK AT INSECTS AND CREEPIE-CRAWLIES.
WHAT ARE YOU LOOKING AT ME FOR?
CUTHBERT CRINGEWORTHY, SCHOOL SWOT
Enter Toots—
I FOUND THIS FIRE-FLY, SIR.
JOLLY GOOD . . .
. . . MY BIKE LIGHT ISN'T WORKING—THIS WILL DO INSTEAD!
HUH!
WHAT KIND OF INSECT'S THIS?
LET ME HAVE A CLOSER LOOK.
BUT IT WOULD TAKE YOU ABOUT THREE HOURS TO CLEAN YOUR SHOES EVERY MORNING!
PUFF!
POLISH
WHAT HAVE YOU GOT IN THAT MATCHBOX, SMIFFY?
A QUEEN BEE!
AH! DID YOU KNOW THAT ALL THE OTHER BEES SWARM TO THE QUEEN BEE, WHEREVER SHE IS?
Meanwhile—
MUST SHOW TEACHER THIS HANDSOME DRAGONFLY.
CLASS IIB
CLASS IIB
HEY, TEACHER—ERK!
AARGH! THAT FACE! LET'S BUZZ OFF!
YAHOO! WELL DONE, PLUG!

F YOU GO AND SEE IF YOU CAN FIND ANY INSECTS TO STUDY.
RIGHT!
Later—
WHAT HAVE YOU GOT THERE, DANNY?
PYONNNNNG!
A FLEA!
SCRATCH!
GET OUT, YOU LITTLE HORROR!
SCRATCH!
ARE YOU TALKING TO ME OR THE FLEA?
HE SEEMS TO HAVE COME QUITE ATTACHED TO YOU, TEACHER!
PRANG!
YEOW! IT'S AN EARWIG!
SMASHING CENTIPEDE, EH?
IMAGING HAVING ALL THOSE LEGS—YOU'D BE ABLE TO RUN REALLY FAST!
LIKE THAT, YOU MEAN?
EH?
AHOO! THERE'S OUR UEEN, PALS!
RARE WHIZZ-BEES
BZZZZ!
BZZZZZ!
BZZZ!
BZZZZ!
HELP! RUN!
OH, DEAR! WE WON'T BE ABLE TO GET BACK IN THE CLASSROOM!
BZZZZ!
BZZZZ!
BZZZZ!
THAT'S OK, TEACHER—WE DON'T MIND!
STAY AS LONG AS YOU LIKE, BEES!
BZZZZ!
BZZZZZ!
BAH! PLUG, WHAT A THING TO DO!
Back in class—
WOW! THE BEES HAVE MADE THEIR HIVE IN MY DESK! WHIZZ-BEES EVEN MAKE HONEY FAST!
Soon—
ANYONE FOR ANOTHER HONEY SANDWICH?
CHOMP! YES, PLEASE, TEACHER!
CHOMP! CHEW! YOU'RE FORGIVEN, PLUG!

ON YOUR BIKE
ALL READY FOR OUR CYCLE RIDE IN THE COUNTRY?
YES, SIR!
BICYCLE SHED
CYCLES—HO!
But—
JOINER'S YARD
OOPS!
Meanwhile—
LOVELY VIEW FROM UP HERE.
GLOOMF!
So—
ON GUARD!
CLICK!
CLUNK!
SNARL!
WHEE! I CAN REALLY GO FAST ON THIS UNICYCLE!
But—
HE MUST NEED A BATH BADLY!
SPLOOSH!
STICK
Soon—
FINE DAY FOR A PEACEFUL CYCLE RUN ON YOUR OWN.
ON MY OWN?
OH, NO! MIGHT HAVE GUESSED THIS WOULD HAPPEN!

SILLY SMIFFY! YOUR BIKE'S STILL ON ITS STAND!
GASP! PUFF! WHEEZE!
WHIRRR!
CHOMP! MUNCH!
CREAK!
GROAN!
I'LL TAKE A SHORT-CUT.
DRIVE FURTHER ON RUBBERO TYRES
H! THIS IS HE ROAD.
OOF!
SPLAT!
YOU AREN'T PEDALLING HARD ENOUGH!
I AM SO! IT'S YOU WHO'S SLACKING!
LIKE MY SUPER AIR-HORN?
HONK! HONK!
SQUEEZE
HONK-HONK! AN INVADER IN MY TERRITORY!
WILD GOOSE (VERY WILD)
HONK! HONK!
GET OUT OF IT!
NIP
Later—
I'VE SOLVED THE PROBLEM— THEY WON'T GET LOST AGAIN!
WHIRRR!
WE'LL HAVE OUR CYCLE RUNS IN THE CLASS-ROOM!
WHIRRR!
WHIRRR!
WHIRRR!
WHIRRR!

FOOTBALL CRAZY
Geography lesson—
WHERE IS MONGOLIA?
BLANK LOOKS
I'LL HAVE TO SHOW YOU, I SUPPOSE.
So—
I'VE GOT CODE NUMBERS FOR ALL THESE MOVES I'VE PLANNED.
COACH
So—
CHINESE RESTAURANT
MENU
WE PLAY CHINA FIRST —READY, FELLOWS?
TIME TO TRY OUT SOME OF MY MOVES.
Later—
OUR NEXT MATCH IS AGAINST FRANCE. YOU STAY HERE, TEACHER.
OK!
BASH ST SCHOOL
Later still—
OH, DEAR! NO NEED TO TAKE DEFEAT SO HARD.
SOB! SOB!
BUT WE WON! BOO-HOO!
THAT'S WHO WE WERE PLAYING—ALL THESE ONIONS HAD US IN TEARS!
WEEPY ONIONS
. . . PLAY FOR A DRAW!
I'LL KNOCK THEM FLYING WITH MY HARDEST SHOT!
So—
LOOK, THE BALL'S BEEN KNOCKED OUT OF SHAPE!
WHAP!

WHERE IS BRITAIN, FRANCE, AMERICA, RUSSIA AND EVERYWHERE ELSE FOR THAT MATTER? SOMEONE'S TAKEN THE GLOBE!
WE'VE GOT IT!
WE'RE PLAYING OUR OWN WORLD CUP MATCHES AND THIS MAKES A PERFECT BALL!
Later—
I'LL BE COACH, TO HELP YOU PLAN YOUR MOVES.
CLASS II B
COACH
28! 7! 14! 19!
HERE'S THE FOOD YOU ORDERED!
ERK! THEY THOUGHT I WAS ORDERING NUMBERS OF DISHES FROM THE MENU!
28
7
14
19
GROAN! THINK I'LL GIVE UP AS COACH—TOO EXPENSIVE!
CHOMP! NEVER MIND! WE SCORED NINETEEN GOALS WHILE THEY WERE FETCHING THE FOOD!
WE COULD HAVE A TOUGH GAME IN THE FINAL.
WHO DO YOU PLAY?
COACH
CHANGING ROOMS
AUSTRALIA—THEY'RE TRAINED KANGAROOS FROM THE CIRCUS!
BOING!
BOING!
BOING!
COACH
THEY'RE GOOD! WE'VE ONLY GOT ONE CHANCE . . .
GOAL!
HEH-HEH! HE HIT THE BALL SO HARD IT BECAME BOOMERANG-SHAPED!
At the final whistle—
WE ARE THE CHAMPIONS!
PHEEP!
YAHOO!

STARSTRUCK
HOROSCOPES BY GYPSY ROSE OLIVE
TAURUS ~ JANITOR
JANITOR
Put your feet up and relax. You may reach new heights today.
MY SHARP CLAWS WILL GET THE LAZY SLOB MOVING!
THIS WAY UP
BREAKFAST TV
JANITOR'S MOUSE
FATMAN
J
JANITOR'S BEANO COLLECTION
WINSTON
EMPTY BREAKFAST BOWL
EMPTY MOG
The benefits of sharing will be obvious today. Your lucky colour is 'red spots' and your lucky number is five (days off school).
MEGA-POSH CHAIR!!
DOCTOR'S NOTE
MEASLES
GEMINI ~ TOOTS & SIDNEY

PERFECT PRESENTS
Things some of the Kids got for their birthdays
AHA! A BALACLAVA!
HAPPY BIRFDAY
BIRTHDAY GREETINGS
HUMPH! WHY DOESN'T IT HAVE A HOLE IN THE FRONT?
THIS IS HANDY . . .
SPOT REMOVER
A SQUEEZ-ZIT AND POPPIT PRODUCT
. . . FOR REMOVING GRAVY SPOTS! WHAT ELSE? HO-HO!
HAPPY BIRTHDAY SPOTTY
SPLAT!
WOW! SUPER!
ALWAYS WANTED A HAT!
HAPPY EASTER
PERFECT . . .
HOW TO DIET
. . . FOR KNOCKING APPLES OUT OF THE TREE!
WHOOOSHH!
YUK!
HAPPY BIRTHDAY
BIRFDAY FUN
HORRIBLE!
MAYBE NOT — MAKES THE PERFECT SWING!
WAHEY!

NO PROBLEM
CAN'T REMEMBER WHERE I PUT MY GLASSES.
SCRATCH!
I REMEMBER NOW . . .
CRUNCH!
THINK I CAN SOLVE YOUR PROBLEM. TOOTS, LEND ME YOUR RIBBON.
TUG
ERK!
NOW, A COUPLE OF MAGNIFYING GLASSES.
THINK I CAN SOLVE YOUR PROBLEM.
I POLISHED MY HEAD THIS MORNING!
WHAT'S WRONG, SPOTTY?
GLUM
I'M FED UP HAVING SPOTS.
I'VE SOLVED YOUR PROBLEMS . . .
. . . NOW YOU CAN SOLVE MINE!
AW!
SUMS QUESTIONS
THERE!
QUESTION
HOW MANY FEET IN A YARD?
ANSWER
Depends how many people are standing in the yard.

...I PUT THEM ON MY SEAT FOR SAFETY!
WHAT WILL I DO, TEACHER? I CAN'T SEE WITHOUT MY SPECTACLES!
MAN'S ANCESTOR
SO I NOTICE!
AH! I CAN SEE PERFECTLY! THANKS, TEACHER!
Soon—
WONDER IF I'M AS HANDSOME AS EVER?
STOP! NO!
SHATTER!
HOW CAN I COMB MY HAIR WITHOUT A MIRROR?
I KNOW—GO AND HELP THE JANITOR CLEAN OUT THE COALSHED.
So—
THANKS, TEACHER—CAN'T SEE MY SPOTS NOW!
GOOD, EH?
QUESTION
WHAT'S THE SQUARE ROOT OF 64?
ANSWER
A tree - it's the only thing with roots I know of.
SLURP!
QUESTION
IF YOU CATCH A TRAIN AT 12.00 AND IT TRAVELS AT 60 M.P.H., WHAT TIME WILL IT ARRIVE AT A TOWN 120 MILES AWAY?
ANSWER
Don't care, as long as it has a buffet car.
WHAT A PROBLEM CLASS!

BULLY for YOU
THERE'S A NEW BOY ARRIVING TODAY.
WONDER WHAT HE'LL BE LIKE?
OUT OF MY WAY, WORMS!
HOI!
OOOF!
SHOVE
PUSH
MY NAME'S NICHOLAS NASTY—NASTY BY NAME AND BY NATURE
YOU CAN CARRY MY BOOKS!
THUMP!
THAT'S NOT FAIR!
OH, NO?
YOU CAN CARRY ME THEN!
GASP! THIS IS HARD WORK!
PUFF!
In class—
HAW-HAW!
NOW HE'S FOR IT!
daft teacher
WHO DREW THAT?
ME! SO WHAT?
ER—WELL—EM—
PONK!
THE SCHOOL'S NEW CLOCK TOWER'S TO BE DELIVERED BY HELICOPTER TODAY.
COAL CELLAR
AHA!
WHIRR!
LOOK, NICHOLAS!
YOU ARE FEELING SLEEPY—VERY, VERY SLEEPY!

DO YOUR FRIENDS CALL YOU NICK?
I DON'T HAVE ANY FRIENDS!
NICE BADGE YOU'VE GOT. WHAT DOES IT SAY?
THAT'S WHAT IT SAYS!
GULP!
SCHOOL BULLY
'M HUNGRY...
..YOU CAN GIVE ME A SNACK!
RUMBLE!
CHOC
CHOMP! CHEW! GUZZLE!
HOPE TEACHER CAN SORT OUT THAT BULLY!
SCHOOL
WHAT A TALENTED ARTIST YOU ARE! KEEP IT UP!
WHAT ARE WE GOING TO DO ABOUT NICHOLAS?
WE COULD HYPNOTISE HIM WITH A WATCH!
TINKLE!
NO USE—HIS TOUGH STARE WOULD SHATTER THE WATCH!
PYONNG!
THUNDEROUS SNORES!
U WILL OBEY ME . . . YOU ARE AS GENTLE AS A LAMB!
I THINK IT'S WORKED!
SWEETEST OF SMILES
BAA-BAA!
HAR-HAR! HE SHOULD BE MILES FROM HERE BEFORE HE COMES OUT OF HIS TRANCE!
GAMBOL
LAST WE'LL SEE OF HIM!

Cheeky Chappy
WITH THE BASH STREET PUPS
Coo!
Did you see that bulldog's face, Bones? All baggy!. Yugh!
Not like me! I've no wrinkles at all!
LATER—
Someone's thrown away a trumpet. I'll give you a tune.
BUT—
Funny!
SILENCE
I'll blow harder!
Huh! Someone had stuck a cork in it!
PARP!
KLANG!
BACK AT THE BIN—
Dinner's ready.
I'm starving!
CHOMP!
MANY MOUTHFULS LATER —
ULP! Can't swallow!
Daft dog! Your collar's too tight! There!
I've stretched my cheeks too much today!
He's not a bulldog—he's a fool dog!

BASH STREET SCHOOL
Magazine
FREE TO ALL BEANO FANS!
BASH STREET KIDS MAGAZINE
*NEWS–GOOD and BAD
*LETTERS TO THE EDITOR (Danny)
*PIN-UPS
*SPORTING NEWS
*COOKERY HINTS

UNPOPULAR

Dear Danny,

My problem is that all of the other pupils of IIb dislike me. Can it be because I always do my homework on time and get it all correct?

Yours troubled,
Cuthbert.

Dear Cuthbert,

You're disliked so much not for doing your homework — but for not letting the rest of the pupils copy it before going into class.

Yours answeringly,
Danny.

HANDSOME

Dear Danny,

My problem is that I have people in school staring at me all of the time. I know they do this because I'm so handsome — but it does get a little embarrassing at times.

Yours big-headedly,
Plug.

Dear Plug,

My answer to your problem is — GO FOR AN EYE TEST WITHOUT DELAY!

Yours tellingly,
Danny.

"Take one screwdriver, screws and two six inch bolts. Screw bolts in place and fix with stout padlocks just before cooking lunch.

This stops your 'victims' escaping before they've eaten whatever you have cooked"!

"Heh-heh!"

A KNOCKOUT PIN-UP

EMPLOYMENT

TEACHER WANTED

Must be kind, gentle and very weak willed. Must like handing out free sweets instead of homework.

Apply in person to The Bash Street Kids Class IIb.

COOK WANTED

Anyone who can make a meal which will stay on a plate and not crash through the table is welcomed.

Apply The Bash Street Kids.

ARTICLES FOR SALE

***** ***Great heaps of unused school books. Cheap for quick sale. Box IIb.***

***** ***One class swot. Answers to the name 'Cuthbert'. Free to good home.***

ARTICLES WANTED

Beanos. Lots of them. Willing to pay *ANY* price. BASH STREET KIDS

PETS CORNER

Winston and Goldie the Goldfish.

SPORTING NEWS

RECORD BROKEN

BASH ST. FOOTBALL

Posh Street School managed a lucky 35-0 win over our own Bash Street School team. "We were robbed" said team captain Danny after the game. "Bit of a mistake putting 'Erbert in goals."

"We also were one man short in the second half — we couldn't tear Fatty away from the half time oranges," said Danny.

TIDDLYWINKS CHAMPION

Fatty was named the 'Bash Street Tiddlywinks Champion' yesterday after a hard fought contest.

The secret of his success was that he used 'winks' made from custard by the school cook." They certainly were hard and could be 'fired' some distance!" said Fatty. And would he use them again next year to defend his title, he was asked.

"Burp! No — I've just eaten them!" was his reply.

WATCH THIS SPACE
WITH THE BASH STREET PUPS
BUMP!
THUD!
Groan!
Oow!
We keep bumping into each other in our dark bin!
LATER ~
Oh, no! This simply won't do!
All the neighbours will see my rubbish in this clear bin!
We'll take it off your hands!
SO ~
Just what we need!
What a fine, light bin this is!
BUT ~
WHOOSH!
SUDDEN GUST
WHOOPS!
SLAM!
BLOW
STRONG WIND
HELP!
SOON ~
We've got a light bin, ok ~ so light we're in orbit!
US
Lucky we can tow them back!

TRAVEL
GUIDE
One morning—
WE'RE HERE! DIDN'T THINK THE OLD BUS WOULD MAKE IT!
SCHOOL
BASH ST. SCHOOL
BRAKE
SCREECH TO HALT!
WHATEVER YOU DO, DON'T . . .
So, next day—
I'LL USE MY DENNIS THE MENACE BOUNCER!
BOING!
BOING.
BOING!
BOING!
But—
OOPS!
BOING!
BOING!
BOING!
BOING!
BURST!
SWOOSH!
FIZZZZZZ!
SERVES HIM RIGHT FOR WAKING ME UP!
READER'S VOICE
THAT'S MORE LIKE HIM!
HI, SMIFFY!
HI, SMIFFY!
BETTER WAVE BACK.
WAVE
CRUMP!
WAVE
OOF!
YAHOO! I'M TRAVELLING BY HANG-GLIDER!
FATTY'S DAD'S SHED
SNAP!
SNAP!
PERHAPS I SHOULDN'T HAVE HAD TWENTY PLATEFULS OF PORRIDGE!
GLUMF!

SLAM!
...SLAM THE DOOR!
CRASH!
SCHOOL
CLATTER!
BOUNCE!
TINKLE!
DONK!
So—
JOE'S SCRAP YARD
SCHOOL
YOU'LL HAVE TO FIND ANOTHER METHOD OF TRANSPORT TO SCHOOL TOMORROW.
SUPER BIKE, EH?
GLURK!
WHEEEE!
SUDDEN STOP
I'LL USE THESE.
READER'S VOICE
REMARKABLY SENSIBLE FOR SMIFFY!
WE'LL GO BY HORSE!
WRONG! YOU'LL GO BY AIR!
OOF!
URF!
BASH!
THUD!
OH, DEAR!
BASH ST. SCHOOL
SCHOOL NURSE
PUFF! PANT!
PUFF! WHEEZE! THIS ISN'T QUITE THE TRANSPORT I HAD IN MIND!

A LOT OF DOUGH
DOUGHNUT FACTORY
HAW-HAW-HAW! HEE-HEE-HEE!
WHO'S THAT LAUGHING?
IT'S THE FACTORY OWNER.
HAR-HAR-HAR! CHUCKLE! CHUCKLE!
BEANO
HEY! YOU'RE THE BA STREET KIDS! I'M A GREAT FAN OF YOUR
Soon—
THINK I'LL FEED THE DUCKS.
DUCK POND
RATHER DAFT
HOPE THIS DOESN'T MAKE THEM SWIM ROUND IN CIRCLES!
WHIRL
IDIOT! YOU'RE MEANT TO LET GO OF THE DOUGHNUT!
DUCK POND
Shortly—
ICE RINK
COME AND SEE A STAR SKATER IN ACTION.
CUTHBERT CRINGEWORTHY - SCHOOL KNOW-ALL
Inside—
SUCH GRACE! SUCH STYLE!
But—
OO! I FEEL DIZZY!
BETTER GIVE CUTHBERT HIS MARKS, EH?
PONK!
CLASS II B
...HOOPLA!
Then—
OOPS! MISSED!
CLASS II B
GLURK!
GIVE ME THOSE!

HELP YOURSELVES TO SOME DOUGHNUTS.
YUM-YUM!
So—
GREAT THINGS, DOUGHNUTS!
HELP!! CAN'T SWIM!
SOON SAVE YOU!
GREAT LIFE-BELT, EH?
NOTHING POINT NOTHING, NOTHING POINT NOTHING, NOTHING POINT NOTHING . . .
GROAN!
At school—
CLASS II B
HEY! TEACHER'S NOT IN. WE COULD PLAY A GAME OF . . .
HEAD
OH, DEAR! WHAT CAN I DO TILL I GET A NEW PAIR OF GLASSES?
BETTER THAN NOTHING, I SUPPOSE!

POTTY PROVERBS
TURN THE PAGE UPSIDE DOWN TO COMPLETE THE FOLLOWING WELL KNOWN SAYINGS
TOO MANY COOKS SPOIL THE
GLUTTON!
REALLY, YOU SPOIL ME, CHAPS!
PEOPLE IN GLASS HOUSES SHOULDN'T THROW
PARTIES!
CRASH!
A STITCH IN TIME SAVES
LESSONS!
HEY! SAVE SOME FOR THE HEAD'S BOARD!
BAH! I'M STUCK!
ROTTEN EGGS
DON'T PUT ALL YOUR EGGS IN ONE
MORTAR-BOARD!

A BIRD IN THE HAND IS WORTH TWO
HUNDRED-LINES!
LOOK BEFORE YOU
SLEEP!
Z
Z
HEH-HEH!
TEACHER'S A TWIT!
TAKE TWO HUNDRED LINES FOR TEACHING THAT BIRD TO SAY THAT!
MANY HANDS MAKE LIGHT
BASKETS!
GRAB
YOU CAN'T HAVE YOUR CAKE AND
DUMPLINGS!
BURP! THAT'S 'COS I'VE EATEN THEM ALL!
OUT OF SIGHT, OUT OF
SCHOOL!
BASH STREET SCHOOL
WHERE ARE THOSE KIDS?
?
CHORTLE!

RIGHT ON CUE
CUP-BOARD
I'VE GOT A CHOICE FOR YOU TODAY, CHILDREN . . .
. . . MATHEMATICS OR CLEANING ATTICS!
MATHS
HMM! THE CUES AREN'T UP TO MUCH!
CHOMP!
Downstairs—
TEACHER, WE WANT THE CANE!
EH?
HAVE YOU BEEN NAUGHTY?
TURN OUT YOUR POCKETS!
BOYLK!
EH?
SNIP!
SNIP!
I'LL SEW THESE BACK IN YOUR TROUSERS LATER!
CAN'T REACH THE BALL!
So—
CLICK!
CLICK!
CLICK!
CLICK!
And—
Soon—
WONDER IF THEY'VE CLEARED AWAY ALL THE DUST?
WOW! THEY HAVE!

WHEN DO WE START CLEANING?
So—
NO-ONE'S BEEN UP HERE FOR YEARS—LOOK AT ALL THE DUST!
WOW! AN OLD SNOOKER TABLE!
BLOW!
WE DON'T WANT WHACKED, WE JUST WANT TO BORROW IT!
CLICK!
CRUMP!
OO! OW! YOW!
HMM! THESE NEED REPLACED!
YOU NEED A REST!
NICE OF YOU TO OFFER, PLUG!
ERK!
WATCH ME COPY MY HERO—HURRICANE HIGGINS!
EH-HEH! HURRICANE PLUG BLEW ALL THE DUST AWAY!
HOW CAN I REWARD YOU?
I KNOW!
CHOMP!
SLURP!
SLOO!
CLICK!
CLICK!
CLICK!
BULL'S EYES
BULL'S EYES

CREATURE FEATURE
TODAY'S LESSON IS NATURE STUDY.
OH, GOODY, BECAUSE . . .
CLASS II B
PONG! PONG!
. . . WE'VE BROUGHT OUR PETS!
SPLENDID!
One change of wet clothes later—
AH! RABBITS SHOW THEIR WHITE TAILS WHEN THEY'RE SCARED.
THUMP! THUMP!
HELLO THERE, LITTLE BUNNY!
AND YOU CAN SEE WHAT'S FRIGHTENED IT!
ANYONE KNOW WHA KIND OF MOUSE THIS IS?
YOU WERE SAYING, TEACHER?
GASP!
ZOOM!
HAR-HAR! FOOLED YOU!
CLOCK-WORK CAR
SOME PARROTS IMITATE WHAT YOU SAY.
SOME PARROTS IMITATE WHAT YOU SAY.
SO IT WAS YOU SPEAKING ALL THE TIME, WILFRID! COULDN'T SEE YOUR LIPS MOVE FOR YOUR JERSEY!
SQUAWK!
PROD
OOPS! WHAT A GIVEAWAY!
Then—
TRINNG!
AH! INTERVAL!
RATTLE!
CARE FOR TEA AND BUNS IN MY STUDY, TEACHER?
CLASS II B
HOW KIND!

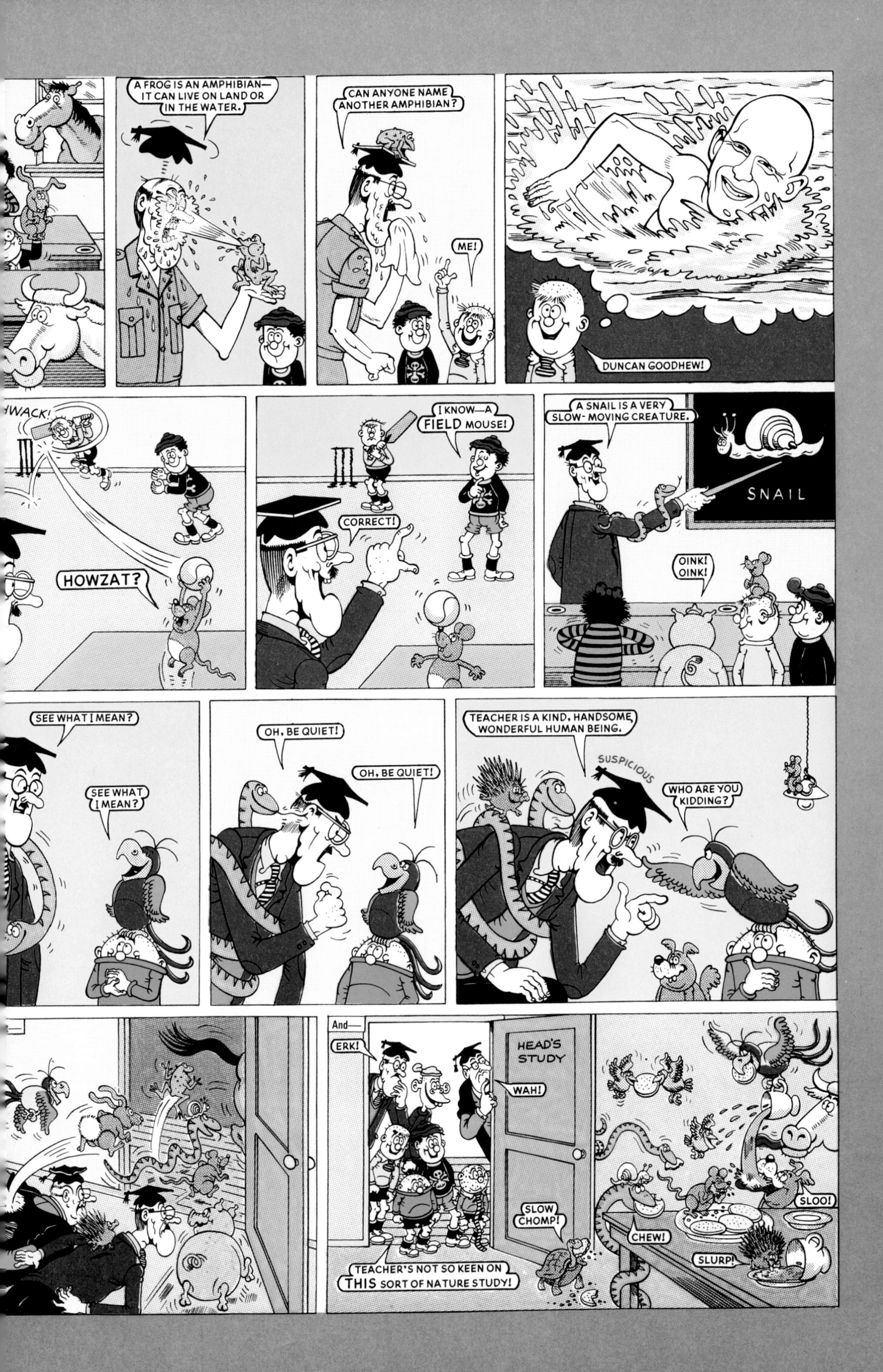

A FROG IS AN AMPHIBIAN— IT CAN LIVE ON LAND OR IN THE WATER.
CAN ANYONE NAME ANOTHER AMPHIBIAN?
ME!
DUNCAN GOODHEW!
HOWZAT?
I KNOW—A FIELD MOUSE!
CORRECT!
A SNAIL IS A VERY SLOW-MOVING CREATURE.
SNAIL
OINK! OINK!
SEE WHAT I MEAN?
SEE WHAT I MEAN?
OH, BE QUIET!
OH, BE QUIET!
TEACHER IS A KIND, HANDSOME, WONDERFUL HUMAN BEING.
SUSPICIOUS
WHO ARE YOU KIDDING?
And—
ERK!
HEAD'S STUDY
WAH!
SLOW CHOMP!
CHEW!
SLURP!
SLOO!
TEACHER'S NOT SO KEEN ON THIS SORT OF NATURE STUDY!

OUT OF SIGHT
BRR! COLD TODAY.
HMM! ONE OF US IS MISSING.
SILLY BOY
ONE, FIVE, THREE, NINE, SIX, TWO, TEN, EIGHT—'ERBERT'S NOT HERE!
OH, DEAR! 'ERBERT CAN'T SEE VERY WELL WITH HIS GLASSES—WHO KNOWS WHAT HE MIGHT DO WITHOUT THEM!
BETTER FOLLOW HIM.
At 'Erbert's house—
HERE'S YOUR LUNCH, DOGGIE.
'ENRY
IDIOT! THAT'S A BRUSH, NOT A DOG!
OOPS! SILLY ME!
'ENRY
Inside—
Next—
YUM! I FANCY A NICE MEAT PIE.
HOI! LEAVE ME ALONE!
NIP!
MUST FEED MY GOLD-FISH.
ANTS EGGS
NONSENSE! I'M AN EXPERT.
NOW TO TAKE AIM . . .
HOI! LET ME GO!
AH! THERE YOU ARE, TIDDLES.

n—
THERE HE IS.
HI, SANTA—NOT FINISHED YOUR CHRISTMAS ROUND YET?
WHY DO YOU HAVE A CAT ON YOUR HEAD, AND WHERE ARE YOUR GLASSES?
ZZZ!
CAT? I THOUGHT IT WAS MY FURRY HAT! I'VE LOST MY GLASSES, YOU SEE.
ER MIND, PUP—I'LL
KE YOU A WALK TO
MAKE UP FOR IT.
OH, NO! THAT'S A RUG, DIM-EYED DOLT!
Later—
WHAT ARE YOU DOING IN THE HOUSE?
SEWING BOX
YOU SHOULD BE HIBERNATING, SILLY HEDGEHOG!
HOI! IN HERE!
HERE YOU ARE, GOLDIE.
Then—
FANCY A GAME OF DARTS, PALS?
WITH YOU? A BIT DANGEROUS!
ERK! I'M OFF!
HIS GLASSES—THERE THEY ARE!
YAHOO!
THANK GOODNESS!
CHEER!
YIP-YIP, HOORAY!
HE'S FOUND THEM!
SILLY ME! I PUT THEM ON MY HEAD WHEN I HAD A NAP!

STARSTRUCK
HOROSCOPES BY GYPSY ROSE OLIVE
CANCER ~ WILFRID
THUD!
OOF! WHO LEFT THIS BAG HERE?
Be careful to hide your feelings when misfortune befalls another.
CHORTLE! GUESS WHO'S GRINNING UNDER THIS JERSEY.
Don't let work get on top of you. Your unlucky colours are black and blue.
THWANG!
THUD!!
RROOAAR!
LEO ~ WINSTON

Barking Mad
WITH THE BASH STREET PUPS
What's this?
A PEA BRAIN
It's a parking meter, little dog.
Gasp! Is it?
BARK! BARK! A pesky cat!
Oops! Better put my money in!
WOOF! WOOF! It's my master, Smiffy!
Hello, my pet pussy cat!
JUST AS DAFT
This is losing me a fortune!
ROWF! ROWF! One of our rivals, a Blob Street dog!
RASP!
Stupid me!
That's the last of my money!
What are you doing, Sniffy?
Putting money in the barking meter! I've just barked!
Daft dog! It's a parking meter — for cars, not dogs!
I'll give him a refund!

NOISE
ANNOYS
HERE THEY COME!
SOUND LIKE DISTANT THUNDER!
BUST OF HEADMASTER
BUMP!
CLUMP!
THUNDER!
IS THAT ANY BETTER, TEACHER?
SLIDE
WHOOPS!
BUMP!
NICE OF YOU TO MAKE US AN INDOOR BOWLS RINK!
Later—
I'VE ANOTHER PLAN.
THESE RUBBER SOLES OUGHT TO KEEP YOU LOT QUIET.
SQUIRT!
RUBBER SOLES
SIGH! I'LL NEVER GET THEM TO WALK QUIETLY.
Then—
TIPTOE
TIPTOE
TIPTOE
EH? GASP! I DON'T BELIEVE IT! WHAT'S COME OVER THEM?
I'VE LOST FERGUS, PET FLEA—MUSTN STEP ON HIM.

TOP STAMPING YOUR FEET!
WHAT WAS THAT, TEACHER? CAN'T HEAR YOU FOR THE NOISE OUR FEET ARE MAKING!
THUMP!
STAMP!
TAKE YOUR SHOES OFF AT THE FRONT DOOR BEFORE YOU COME IN TOMORROW.
TRING!
So, next day—
PONK
KICK
PERHAPS IF I HAD A CARPET FITTED THEIR STAMPING FEET WOULD BE LESS NOISY.
So—
LOVELY GREEN CARPET.
CLUNK!
, DEAR! THINK I'VE PUT CORRECT ANSWER TO HIS SUM—THE KIDS'LL CALL ME A SWOT!
FATTY! WHAT ARE YOU DOING?
THIS SOLE MAKES A GREAT RUBBER!
AARGH! MORE NOISE THAN EVER!
CRUMP!
CRASH!
ERK! I THINK I'VE FOUND HIM!
GOOD OLD TEACHER!
REALLY, TEACHER—STOP STAMPING AROUND!
DREADFUL NOISE! WHAT AN EXAMPLE! TSK! TSK!
STAMP!

SMILES FOR TILES
AH! THE CHILDREN ARE HOLDING THE DOOR OPEN FOR ME.
SLATES FROM SCHOOL ROOF
BONK!
OOMF! OH, NO, THEY'RE NOT!
SLAM!
TWANG!
TWANG!
PLINK! PONK!
HAW-HAW!
NOT BAD!
Next—
GREAT JUGGLING, TOOTS! BRAVO!
CLAP!
WHERE DID TOOTS LEARN TO JUGGLE?
I WAS TRYING TO GET RID OF THESE PESKY ANTS ON THE STAGE!
STAMP!
STAMP!
Next act—
I SAY! I SAY! WHAT'S THE DIFFERENCE BETWEEN AN AFRICAN ELEPHANT AND AN INDIAN ELEPHANT?
ABOUT THREE THOUSAND MILES! BOOM! BOOM!
AWFUL!
BOO!
Finally—
LET US ALL JOIN IN A ROUSING CHORUS OF THE SCHOOL SONG!
BASH STREET, BASH STREET, IT'S A SCHOOL THAT'S HARD TO BEAT . . .
. . . GIVE YOUR KIDS A REAL TREAT, SEND THEM DOWN TO BASH STREET!

Head and Teacher inspect the damage—
WE NEED A NEW ROOF FOR THE SCHOOL, BUT WE'VE NO FUNDS.
LET'S HOLD A FUND-RAISING CONCERT AT THE TOWN HALL.
So—
SMIFFY AND PLUG WILL NOW PLAY YOU A TUNE.
SILLY BOYS! WHERE ARE YOUR MUSICAL INSTRUMENTS?
WE DON'T NEED ANY!
FISH AND CHIPS
FRYING TONIGHT
SIZZLE!
HOT
SHE FETCHES THE FAMILY'S FISH SUPPERS EVERY WEEK!
Then—
RAT-A-TAT-A-TAT!
SUPER TAP-DANCING! CHEER!
TAP-DANCING?
RAT-TAT-TAT!
IF YOU'RE GOING TO THROW ME GRUB, I'LL TELL MORE JOKES!
HOW DO YOU START A GLOW-WORM RACE?
READY—STEADY— GLOW!
AAGH! MUST GET AWAY FROM THESE HORRIBLE BOOKS!
THAT'S GOT RID OF THAT BAD JOKER!
HOW TO SLIM
STOP BEING A FATSO
DIETING MADE EASY
GET THIN
HEEEEE!
SCHOOL
Later—
WELL, THE SCHOOL'S GOT ITS NEW ROOF.
YES, ONLY ONE PROBLEM . . .
SCHOOL
. . . NOW WE HAVE TO HAVE ANOTHER CONCERT!
ROOFLESS
BASH ST. SCHOOL NOTICE BOARD
CONCERT IN AID OF TOWN HALL ROOF FUND

WHAT A DAY
One morning—
PLEASANT DREAMS!
Then—
WAKE UP, YOU LAZY LUMP—YOU'LL BE LATE FOR SCHOOL!
MRS TEACHER
ENOUGH! YOU'VE NO TIME FOR THAT! OFF TO SCHOOL WITH YOU!
CLUNK! SNATCH
REMEMBER AND BEHAVE YOURSELF, AND DON'T BE LATE HOME—OR ELSE!
IT'S LIKE THIS EVERY MORNING, READERS.
PERHAPS YOU'LL HAVE A QUIET DAY AT SCHOOL, TEACHER.
READER'S VOICE
NO CHANCE!
GROAN! I'M STARVING! CAN'T CONTROL THESE KIDS ON AN EMPTY STOMACH!
I KEEP AN EMERGENCY BREAKFAST SUPPLY IN THIS SAFE—I CAN HARDLY WAIT!
CLICK!
But—
AARGH! FATTY!
'MORNING, TEACHER. MY DAD LENT ME HIS HAMMER AND CHISEL. HOPE YOU DON'T MIND. CHOMP!
Later—
SILENCE
THIS IS THE LIFE—PEACE AND QUIET AT LAST.
IT WAS MY WIFE I SENT FOR! NOW I'VE GOT THE LOT OF THEM OUT OF MY HAIR FOR A WHILE.
STEELY GAZE
Meanwhile—
VERY QUIET IN HERE FOR A CHANGE. WHAT'S GOING ON?
CLASS IIB

HERE'S YOUR MORNING WASH— BREAKFAST IN HALF A MINUTE!
GROAN! WHAT I NEED IS A NICE, BIG BREAKFAST.
STAGGER
BREKKY FLAKES
YUM! THIS LOOKS GOOD!
SEE WHAT I MEAN?
TEE-HEE!
Meanwhile, round the corner—
GIVE THAT FLOOR A GOOD SCRUB, JANITOR.
OK. MY MOP'S NICE AND . . .
. . . SOAPY. OOPS!
HA-HA! FORGET TO WASH, TEACHER?
GLOOP!
AH, WELL! AT LEAST THE IDS DON'T SHOUT AT YOU LIKE YOUR WIFE DOES.
MAYBE NOT, READERS . . .
READER'S VOICE
. . . BUT THE HEAD DOES!
WHY AREN'T YOU AT WORK? WHERE'S MY MORNING TEA? RAGE! RANT!
PITY THERE'S NOTHING I CAN DO ABOUT IT, UNLESS . . .
COO! ANY POST TO GO?
PIGEON POST
YES, THERE IS! PLEASE TAKE A MESSAGE TO . . . WHISPER!
EH? WHERE'S TEACHER? I WANTED TO SHOUT AT HIM FOR FORGETTING MY TEA!
CLASS IIB
OO!
THERE HE IS!
ANTED TO SHOUT AT IM FOR NO REASON AT ALL!
SCHOOL
ULP! GOOD JOB I HAVEN'T MUCH HAIR FOR THEM TO GET INTO!

BEAT the BURGLAR
WHY ARE YOU CLEANING THE TROPHY CUPBOARD, TEACHER?
BECAUSE—COUGH! SPLUTTER!—SOMEBODY'S WON A TROPHY FOR THE FIRST TIME IN YEARS!
TROPHY CABINET
THERE—CUTHBERT CRINGEWORTHY'S WO
THE " BRAIN OF BASH STREET " CUP!
IT WAS NOTHING—MY BRAIN IS SECOND ONLY TO MY MODESTY.
BRAIN OF BASH STREET
THE KIDS ARE PRETTY ALARMING WHEN YOU DON'T KNOW THEM—AND EVEN MORE SO WHEN YOU DO!
BONK!
THIS COULD HELP.
HMM! DANNY LOOKS FAR TOO PLEASANT FOR MY PURPOSES.
NOW, SMIFFY—I'VE GOT A QUESTION FOR YOU . . .
OO-ER!
TAP! TAP!
DIM PUPIL
. . WHAT'S YOUR NAME, SMIFFY?
GULP! THAT'S A TOUGH ONE!
GOLLY! THE ANSWER'S ON THE TIP OF MY TONGUE!
CLICK!
At four o'clock—
IF YOU HEAR LOUD SCREAMS IT'LL BE A BURGLAR AFTER OUR TROPHY!
RIGHT YOU ARE!
A few hours later—
SCHOOL
SCREAM!
AHA! MUST BE A BURGLAR!
BASH STREET SCHOOL
But—
I'M THE HEADMASTER I T
YOU! I WENT IN TO COLLE
MY BICCIE BARREL, AND S
THOSE HORRIBLE FACE

HMM! THAT'S A VERY VALUABLE CUP. I'D HATE IT TO BE STOLEN.
WE NEED A BURGLAR ALARM.
CABINET
GRR! SWOT!
At lunchtime—
HIGH STREET
THERE'S A BURGLAR ALARM SHOP JUST ALONG HERE.
YIKES! THE MOST ALARMING THING ABOUT THESE IS THE PRICE! CAN'T AFFORD THAT!
BURGLAR ALARMS
BARGAIN! ONLY £500
ONLY £400
CHEAP AT £399
I'LL HAVE TO THINK OF A CHEAPER SYSTEM.
DOUBLE HOMEWORK OF HARD SUMS FOR YOU TONIGHT, DANNY!
ARGH! HOW HORRIBLE!
NOW FOR THE REST OF THEM.
I'LL CONFISCATE THAT, FATTY!
GRR! THAT'S MY PRE-SNACK SNACK!
CLICK!
SNATCH
WOULD YOU CARE TO LOOK HANDSOME FOR THE CAMERA, PLUG?
AM I EVER ANYTHING ELSE?
MY POOR CAMERA WOULDN'T HAVE STOOD UP TO IT IF HE'D TRIED TO LOOK UGLY!
CLICK!
So, later—
HOW'S THAT? ANY BURGLAR WHO SEES THIS LOT WILL RUN FOR MILES!
LIKELY STORY! A CRIMINAL TYPE IF EVER I SAW ONE!
TO THE POLICE STATION
YOU IDIOT! DIDN'T YOU KNOW I'D ARRANGED SPECIAL PROTECTION FOR THE CUP?
Later—
WOW! IT'S GNASHER! NO-ONE WOULD DARE STEAL THE CUP WITH HIM IN IT!
ZZZ!
BRAIN OF BASH STREET

STARSTRUCK
HOROSCOPES BY GYPSY ROSE OLIVE
VIRGO ~ CUTHBERT
To my mate Cuthbert, from a fan, John Virgo
CLICK!
VERY HARD EXAM
You will be extremely popular with those around you. Your lucky number is 100 out of 100.
You will receive some good news. Your lucky number is 24 and lucky colour is sort of orangish and your unlucky colour may well be green.
YOU HAVE WON TWO DOZEN CHEESES IN A RAFFLE. Congratulations!
VERY MATURE CHEESE
VERY MATURE MOUSE
1 TON
LIBRA ~ FATTY

CUTHBERT THE COURAGEOUS
Could this be the new, tough Cuthbert?
NO, TEACHER!
I HAVEN'T DONE ENOUGH EXTRA HOMEWORK YET!
Spoke back to Mummy— in harsh tones too!
I WON'T WEAR THESE! I JUST WON'T!
Couldn't hear Cuthbert anyway.
ZRRRMMM!
TITTER! I MUCH PREFER MY 'BUNNY RABBIT' ONES!
HOME SWEETIES HOME
JOLLY WELL WATCH OUT, MISTER SNAKE!
VERY HEROIC LOOK
VERY HEROIC KNEES
I NEED TO BORROW YOU TO KEEP OUT A SHOCKING DRAUGHT AT THE FOOT OF MY BEDROOM DOOR!
FAVOURITE MATHS BOOK

WHEELER DEALER
After a posh dinner—
TOWN HALL
IS YOUR CHAUFFEUR BRINGING YOUR LIMOUSINE, SIR?
BASH STREET SCHOOL HEADMASTER
THIS IS MY CHAUFFEUR!
GASP!
WE'LL DRIVE PAST THE COUNTRY HOUSE OF LORD AND LADY WRIGHT-SNOBBE.
SPLENDID! I LOVE MIXING WITH THE UPPER CLASSES.
HOLD TIGHT! THERE'S A RATHER NASTY . . .
WAH!
Later in the Head's study—
I'VE GOT A GREAT IDEA!
PERFUME
CLASS IIB
COME WITH ME, KIDS—IF YOU HELP ME I'LL GIVE YOU A FREE BICCIE!
AND, IF YOU'RE REALLY GOOD, I'LL GIVE YOU A FREE BICCIE EACH!
HUH! NOT ONLY IS THE HEAD NOT THE MOST GENEROUS MAN IN THE WORLD . . .
So—
NICE AND COMFY—THIS WILL SUIT ME FINE.
ER—HAVEN'T YOU FORGOTTEN ONE LITTLE THING?
THIS CAR'S GOT NO ENGINE—IT WON'T GO ANYWHERE!
OH, YES, IT WILL!

OH, DEAR! YOU REALLY NEED BETTER TRANSPORT, HEAD!
SPLOOSH!
Next morning—
CHUG! CHUG!
AH, TEACHER! I'VE GOT A JOB FOR YOU!
YOU HAVE BEEN GIVEN THE HONOUR OF BEING MY NEW CHAUFFEUR! DRIVE ON!
HMM! I'VE GOT A LITTLE PLAN TO GET OUT OF THIS!
PON MY WORD! IT'S HAT VERY COMMON TTLE HEADMASTER!
AND NOT SO LITTLE! IF HE STAYS IN THE POND THERE'LL BE NO ROOM FOR THE TADPOLES!
Back at school—
MOAN! GROAN!
WHO IS IT? THE ABOMINABLE PONDMAN?
IT'S ME, YOU LITTLE HORRORS!
WOOPS! SORRY, HEAD!
. HE'S NOT THE OST ENERGETIC EITHER!
FASTER—I MUST FIND A CHAUFFEUR-DRIVEN CAR BEFORE THE SHOPS SHUT!
SUPA MOTORS
THOSE DREADFUL KIDS AREN'T GETTING IN HERE!
MINI IN BOOT FOR TOWN DRIVING
GOLD PLATED BUMPERS ETC.
NOT QUITE WHAT I HAD IN MIND!
I SHOULD FIND SOMETHING IN HERE, THOUGH!
I. BASHEM SCRAP METAL DEALERS
UFF!
GASP! PANT!
LAZY, BIG, FAT LUMP!
WE RATHER LIKE BEING CHAUFFEUR DRIVEN!
WHEEZE! WISH I'D STUCK TO THE BIKE!
THAT'S BETTER!

HOT WHEELS
On the way to school—
COUGH!
RATTLE!
RATTLE!
'MORNING TEACHER!
COME WITH US!
At the Go-Kart track—
WE'RE ALLOWED TO DRIVE THERE!
FRED'S GO-KARTS
BET I CAN DO A FASTER LAP THAN YOU!
READY—STEADY—
BRRRM!
BRRM!
NOW I'LL SHOW YOU SOME REAL DRIVING!
Meanwhile—
VROOM!
VROOM!
FRED'S GO-KARTS
WE'LL ALTER THE TRACK A BIT.
LONG TRACK, THIS!
POND
WHAT A DRIVER!
GLUG!
GLUG!
GASPSH!
AMAZING CONTROL!
SCREECH!

Later—
SNORE! GRUNT!
CHUG-CHUG!
ZZZZ
AT LAST! NOT A VERY FAST DRIVER, TEACHER!
IT'S THIS OLD CAR'S FAULT! I'D BE LIKE A GRAND PRIX DRIVER IN THE RIGHT MACHINE!
BET WE COULD OUT-DRIVE YOU!
DON'T BE DAFT—YOU'RE TOO YOUNG TO DRIVE!
GO!
VAROOM!
WHAT TIME DID I DO?
SCREECH OF BRAKES!
I HAVEN'T A CLUE!
I CAN'T SEE A THING FOR THE DIRT YOU SPRAYED UP!
WAAH! WHO PUT THIS HILL HERE?
CRUMP!
THWACK!
ROAR! BELLOW!
OU'RE THE HAMPION!
JUST A MINUTE—MUST DO THE JOB PROPERLY!
GLOOP!
POP
HEH! HEH! I'VE ALWAYS WANTED TO DO THIS!
SWOOSH!
SHAKE

ON THE MAT
WITH THE BASH STREET PUPS
Look at those muddy pawprints!
We need a doormat!
PEA-BRAINED PUP
There's one in this field!
What's this?
SNORE
One doormat!
It's a dormouse! Doormats are bigger!
Oh, I know what Peeps means!
Let me go!
What now?
SNARL!
No! That's a doorMAN!
SO~
WHEEP!
Who whistled for us?
H-HEY!
TRIP
There! Seven doormats!
SPLAT!
Oo-er! Think they want to wipe their paws on ME!
GROWLS!

STARSTRUCK
HOROSCOPES BY GYPSY ROSE OLIVE
SCORPIO ~ TEACHER
5 ton
Queen rules U.K.
Watch your step and don't let people at work get you down. Your unlucky number is 2B.
You don't seem to be getting through to people around you. A friend may be able to help you see things in a different light.
POOR 'ERBET PUT HIS GLASSES DOWN THEN COULDN'T SEE TO FIND THEM!
WHAT DID YOU THINK OF THE GAME ON SATURDAY? EH? EH? I'M SPEAKING TO YOU!
KEEP YOUR DOG ON A LEAD!!
SAGITTARIUS ~ 'ERBERT

WATCH THE BIRDIE
HELLO, READERS! I'VE TAKEN U BIRD-WATCHING. WISH I COUL SPOT A REALLY RARE BIRD.
STUPID SMIFFY! YOU SCATTER BIRD SEED FOR BIRDS TO EAT!
BIRD SEED
SHAKE
HERE THEY COME! HOPE THERE'S A LONG-EYEBROWED MOCKING BIRD AMONG THEM.
BAH! COMMON SPARROWS, BLACKBIRDS, CROWS, PIGEONS, AND...
SOMEHOW I CAN TELL WHO MADE EACH TREE, CAN'T YOU, READERS?
Then—
THINK I'LL SIT ON A TREE AND MOCK THAT CHAP WITH THE GLASSES!
IT'S A LONG-EYEBROWED MOCKING BIRD
YUM! AUNT OLIVE'S COOKING APPLE PIE AND CUSTARD— THIS " TREE'S " STARVING!
SNIFF!
AROM
PIE
FIRST, SOME SPRAY-ON ADHESIVE . . .
SQUIRT!
SQUIRT!
. . . THEM SOME FEATHERS FROM MY DAD'S PIGEON LOFT!
HERE ARE YOUR EYEBROWS!
HORRIBLE FAT LITTLE MAN! CALL YOURSELF A HEADMASTER? MOCK! MOCK!
HEY! AN IMPOSTOR!

ND ME A LONG-EYEBROWED
OCKING BIRD, TEACHER, AND
I'LL GIVE YOU A 10p RISE
IN YOUR WAGES!
PROD
HOW GENEROUS!
MAYBE BIRD SEED WOULD DO THE TRICK.
BIRDS
IT WON'T WORK, TEACHER.
TWEET! TWEET!
TWEET! TWEET!
I PLANTED BIRD SEED IN THESE POTS, AND NOT A SINGLE BIRD CAME UP!
COMMON, EH? WE'RE NOT STAYING HERE TO BE INSULTED!
CHEEK!
PECK! PECK!
AHA! LONG-EYEBROWED MOCKING BIRDS LIKE PLENTY OF TREES.
RIGHT–DISGUISE YOURSELVES AS TREES!
CARD
CARD
RED
BROWN
GREEN
SPLAT!
YIKES! WHO MOVED THE TREE?
COME BACK, BIRDIE! HEAD HASN'T SEEN YOU!
DAZED
I DON'T FEEL VERY WELL!
DON'T WORRY, TEACHER–HEAD WILL GET HIS LONG-EYEBROWED MOCKING BIRD, OK!
ONDERFUL! A LONG-EYEBROWED MOCKING BIRD!
GASP! THE DISGUISE HAS FOOLED HEAD!
CLAP!
No, it hasn't, Teacher—
MAKE A MOCKERY OF ME, WOULD YOU?
EH?
NO LONG-EYEBROWED MOCKING BIRD CAN STAND BEING MOCKED HIMSELF! BE OFF WITH YOU!
HAVE TO WATCH THIS!

COOL SCHOOL
THE HEATING'S BROKEN—IT'S TOO COLD TO WORK IN HERE!
NONSENSE!
Then—
CLASS IIB
TEA'S UP.
AH, LOVELY! I DO LIKE MY CUP OF TEA.
Inside—
WE NEED FEATHERS FOR OUR INDIAN HEAD-DRESSES!
SQUAWK!
PRETTY POLLY! PRETTY POLLY!
UGLY PLUG! UGLY PLUG!
HANDY FOR OPENING MY CAN OF POP!
HOI!
STAB
HISS!
And—
MY WORD IT'S HOT! GASP!
SIZZLE!
TAKE OUT YOUR BOOKS.
FAN
YOU'VE SCORCHED THEM ALL! THIS IS HOPELESS.
SIZZLE!
THUD!
OOF!
OOYAH!
OUCH!
OW!
SAUNA
THIS PLACE IS TOO DANGEROUS!
Later—
BEDDING STORE
CONTINENTAL QUILTS
ALL SIZES
Try one today
AHA!

OO-ER! PERHAPS IT IS RATHER ON THE COLD SIDE!
SCHOOL
COME—WE'LL FIND A WARMER PLACE TO LEARN.
Soon, at the zoo—
TROPICAL BIRD HOUSE
JUST THE PLACE.
SQUAWK! GET OUT!
WE'LL HAVE TO FIND ANOTHER PLACE!
Soon—
BURNING SANDS INDIAN RESTAURANT
HERE WILL DO.
HOT CURRY SMELL
ICE COLD WATER FOR MEDIUM CURRIES
FIRE EXT. FOR EXTRA-HOT CURRIES
ONE EXTRA-HOT CURRY AND ELEVEN FORKS, PLEASE!
SLURP!
SAUNA
IT'LL BE WARM IN HERE.
STEAM AWAY YOUR CARES
In the sauna—
SUPER!
OH, DEAR! MY GLASSES HAVE STEAMED UP!
AND MINE!
MINE, TOO!
LOVELY AND COSY—NOW FOR OUR HISTORY LESSON.
IN 1642 . . . DRONE—DRONE—YAWN!—
SNORE!
ZZZ!
GRUNT!
SNORT!
EDITOR'S VOICE
DON'T WORRY, READERS — I'LL WAKEN THEM UP FOR THE NEXT STORY!

RODENT
STUDENT
ISN'T IT AMAZING . . .
. . . HOW, WHEN ONE CHILD CATCHES AN ILLNES
Then—
HI!
AHA! A PUPIL!
WHAT IS ONE SQUEAK PLUS ONE SQUEAK?
SQUEAK! SQUEAK!
BRAVO! WHAT A CLEVER LITTLE FELLOW—MUCH BRIGHT THAN MY USUAL PUPILS.
CLAP! CLAP! CLAP!
YOU LEARN A LOT WHE YOU LIVE IN THE BAC OF A CLASSROOM.
WHEN WAS THE BATTLE OF BANNOCKBURN?
SCRATCH!
Then—
NIBBLE! NIBBLE! NIBBLE! NIBBLE!
NIBBLE! NIBBLE! NIBBLE!
BRILLIANT!
1314
Enter Winston, the janitor's cat—
AHA!
NO! NO!
R-I-P!
HEH-HEH! THAT'S G RID OF HIM!

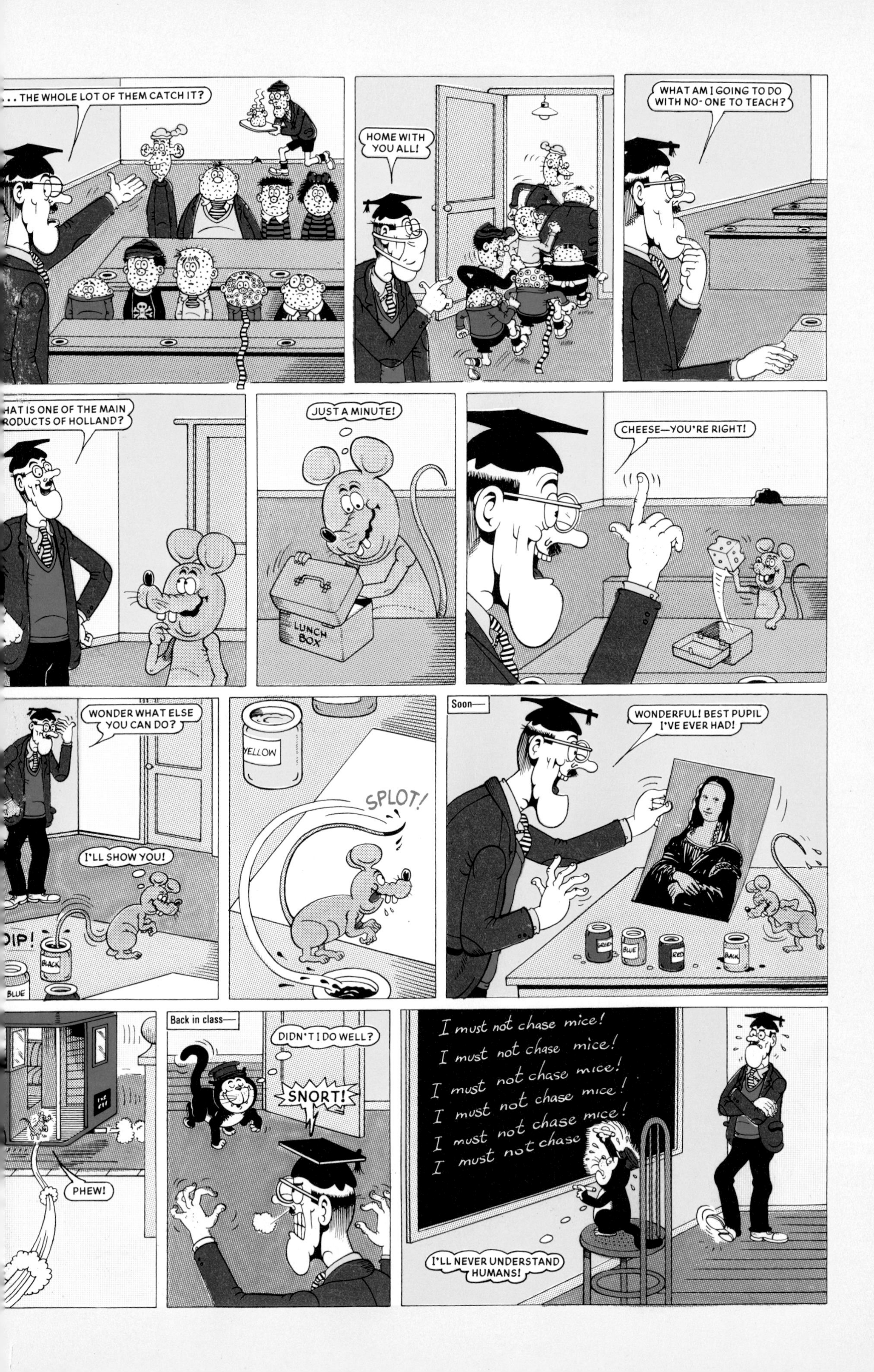
. . . THE WHOLE LOT OF THEM CATCH IT?
HOME WITH YOU ALL!
WHAT AM I GOING TO DO WITH NO-ONE TO TEACH?
HAT IS ONE OF THE MAIN RODUCTS OF HOLLAND?
JUST A MINUTE!
LUNCH BOX
CHEESE—YOU'RE RIGHT!
WONDER WHAT ELSE YOU CAN DO?
I'LL SHOW YOU!
DIP!
BLACK
BLUE
YELLOW
SPLOT!
Soon—
WONDERFUL! BEST PUPIL I'VE EVER HAD!
BLUE
RED
PHEW!
Back in class—
DIDN'T I DO WELL?
SNORT!
I must not chase mice!
I must not chase mice!
I must not chase mice!
I must not chase mice!
I must not chase mice!
I must not chase
I must not chase
I
I'LL NEVER UNDERSTAND HUMANS!

MEAN STREAK
HMM! MUST BE ABOUT TIME . . .
. . . FOR TEA!
YEECH!
HERE'S A SICK ANIMAL FOR YOU!
THAT FACE! I DON'T FEEL WELL!
HOW MEAN CAN YOU GET?
HERE'S YOUR TICKET.
THANKS! OO-ER!
A MOUSTACHE? WHAT A MEAN MAN FOR TRYING TO GET ON FOR HALF FARE!
Next day—
LET'S PLAY A TRICK ON MEAN TEACHER.
That night—
CAN'T STRAIGHTEN UP—THIS IS AWFUL!
YOU MAKE A VERY HANDY TABLE, TEACHER.
CAN'T TAKE MUCH MORE OF THIS!
The Kids arrive—
WE'LL HELP YOU IF YOU PROMISE NOT TO BE MEAN IN THE FUTURE.
ANYTHING! I PROMISE!
HEH-HEH

I'VE USED THIS TEA-BAG TO MAKE 274 CUPS OF TEA!
TEACHER'S VERY MEAN THESE DAYS.
PLOP!
Then—
I'M FROM "THE SICK ANIMALS' SOCIETY". CARE TO CONTRIBUTE?
RATTLE!
ER—EM—WELL—
—JUST A MINUTE . . .
ME TO CATCH THE BUS HOME.
TRINNG!
Then—
SLAM!
On the bus—
A HALF FOR YOU, SONNY?
I'LL GLUE THIS PENNY TO THE GROUND!
MY LUCKY DAY!
CLICK!
YOWL! MY BACK!
BZZ!
YEOW!
JAB!
YOU'VE DONE IT!
STRAIGHTEN UP
And—
EAT ALL YOU WANT!
WHAT A GENEROUS CHAP!
CHOMP!

SNOW FUN
Just before the Christmas holidays—
SCHOOL
I HATE WHEN THERE'S SNOW AND ICE ABOUT.
HEH-HEH!
PLOP! PLOP! PLOP!
SEEN MY GOLF BAG?
MY KETTLE'S MISSING.
SO'S ONE OF MY RUBBER GLOVES!
OLIVE
THERE THEY ARE!
LOOK WHAT THEY'VE MADE—ICED LOLLIES!
TWANG!
CAN'T WAIT!
SHAKE
THIS IS ALL YOUR FAULT!
BAH! I'VE BEEN TRICKED!
TEE-HEE!
YOU'RE TO BLAME—YOU CAN TAKE ME HOME!
Later—
SLURP! SLOO!
HOW I WISH I COULD BE IN THE MIDDLE OF SOME TROPICAL ISLAND.
SHATTERED DREAM
HEY! MAKE YOUR OWN SLIDE, TEACHER!
WHOOSH!

SPLOT!
SPLAT!
SPLUT!
FROZEN WORM
YOU CAN SEE WHY I HATE THESE CONDITIONS.
SCRAPE!
CLASS II B
BRR! I NEED A CUP OF TEA. HEY! WHERE'S MY TEA MUG?
EMPTY SPACE
Later—
BUS STOP
IT'S COLD QUEUING FOR A BUS, TOO!
Then—
BUS STOP
LOCAL BUS
HEY! AREN'T YOU GETTING ON?
TAP
I SAID, AREN'T YOU GETTING ON?
SMACK!
PUFF! PANT!
Shortly—
HEY! THIS ISN'T WHERE I LIVE.
PLUG'S HOUSE
YOU SAID TO PULL YOU HOME— AND THIS IS MY HOME!
WAAAAH!
WHUMP!
FLY TO THE SUN WITH COCONUT AIRWAYS
GROAN!
HEH-HEH! LOOKS LIKE YOU'VE GOT YOUR WISH, TEACHER!

DON'T YOU MISS SEEING THE BASH ST KIDS

•ANSWER• SMIFFY OF COURSE. THAT BOY REALLY IS DAFT!

READING "THE BEANO"?
THE BEANO
DENNIS the MENACE and GNASHER
GNASHEE!
FLAP!
FLAP!
THROW!
GNIPPEE!
TAP!
TAP!
"THE BEANO" EVERY WEEK!
I'M NOT THAT DAFT—I WAS IN THE COAL BUCKET READING MY DENNIS THE MENACE BOOK!

FIRST WE'LL STUDY GEOGRAPHY.
WE'LL STUDY PEOPLE FROM OTHER LANDS.
XOXOX
XOXOX
BRING YOUR SPORTS GEAR . . .
. . . AND SOMETHING TO READ!
THE BEANO BOOK
THE BEANO BOOK
DENNIS the MENACE
DENNIS the MENACE
BEANO